AN INTRODUCTION
TO SOCIAL PSYCHIATRY

AN
INTRODUCTION
TO
SOCIAL
PSYCHIATRY

By

Alexander H. Leighton, M.D.

CHARLES C THOMAS • PUBLISHER
Springfield • Illinois • U.S.A.

CHARLES C THOMAS • PUBLISHER
BANNERSTONE HOUSE
301-327 East Lawrence Avenue, Springfield, Illinois, U.S.A.

Published simultaneously in the British Commonwealth of Nations by
BLACKWELL SCIENTIFIC PUBLICATIONS, LTD., OXFORD, ENGLAND

Published simultaneously in Canada by
THE RYERSON PRESS, TORONTO

© *1960, by* CHARLES C THOMAS • PUBLISHER

Library of Congress Catalog Card Number: 60-11267

With THOMAS BOOKS careful attention is given to all details of
manufacturing and design. It is the Publisher's desire to present books
that are satisfactory as to their physical qualities and artistic possibilities
and appropriate for their particular use. THOMAS BOOKS will be
true to those laws of quality that assure a good name and good will.

Printed in the United States of America

For
Dorothea
the journey's partner
this pause for summing up

FOREWORD

"Social Psychiatry" as a label coming into more and more use tends to have somewhat indefinite meaning; it often represents different things to different people. This book constitutes an attempt to develop a useful definition, one that encompasses common features that link a number of emerging activities in the field of psychiatry.

Part I offers some current examples of what may be thought of as social psychiatry in action, and there is a pointing out of the common features and underlying principles. At the end, suggestions are offered with regard to potentialities for additional development.

Part II extends the definition with a look at research. A selecting review is presented of certain questions that stand open, and of some partial answers now at hand. In conclusion, a number of implications are brought forward that have import for psychiatry and the civilizations of which it is a part.

A.H.L.

ACKNOWLEDGMENTS

The strongest expression of appreciation is due the Salmon Committee for the privilege and opportunity of presenting these talks. The occasion has some personal meaning in that it was as a beginning student of psychiatry under Adolph Meyer in the mid '30s that I became acquainted with the Salmon Lectures. Although not published until recently, the first lectures were used in teaching at John Hopkins and stood high both as an honor and as an achievement. I can only hope that my effort now does not fall too far short of the standards thus set by a former teacher.

The research findings mentioned in Part II are derived from the Stirling County Study of Psychiatric Disorder and Sociocultural Environment. This work was supported by the Milbank Memorial Fund, the Carnegie Corporation of New York, the Department of National Health and Welfare of Canada, and the Department of Public Health of the Province of Nova Scotia.

Critical evaluation of this book has been given by Oskar Diethelm, John S. Harding, Jane M. Hughes and David Macklin, while assistance with bibliography was provided by R. H. Felix, Gertrude Leighton, Donna Regenstreif and Janet Sperber.

Kazuko Smith and Amorita Suarez have prepared the manuscript for publication.

For all this help, I am deeply grateful.

A.H.L.

CONTENTS

AN INTRODUCTION
TO SOCIAL PSYCHIATRY

Part I

ACTIONS AND USES

EXAMPLES OF SOCIAL PSYCHIATRY

Social psychiatry can be employed as a collective term for a variety of activities related to, but not the same as, clinical psychiatry. And, in parenthesis, let us assume we know what clinical psychiatry is, at least well enough so there is no need to pause over the matter. Let us take it to be the diagnosis and treatment of patients—hospital, out-patient service, day clinic, night clinic, and private practice, all included.

Social Psychiatry is not the same as these—but then what is it? What is the collection of activities one could group under this name? I should like to suggest the following as among the candidates.

PSYCHIATRY AND THE LAW

Consider first psychiatry as applied to the courts. This is probably the most ancient form of social psychiatry, although forensic psychiatrists may be surprised and alarmed by the assertion. They are, nevertheless, engaged in the injection of psychiatric knowledge and orientation into one of the procedures whereby society maintains its organization. At its best forensic psychiatry helps enlarge the concept of justice and makes more effective the bringing to bear of treatment and care where these are appropriate.

Closely related to work in the courts is psychiatry as

an aid to the police and in the functioning of prisons.

These several activities are concerned in part with differentiating, and in part with recommendations for handling, people who are psychotic, psychoneurotic, or otherwise suffering from one of the patterns of human behavior commonly recognized as disorder in psychiatric clinics. The activities differ from ordinary clinical work in being a part of the legal and penal systems. They are also different in the frequency of problems involving drug use, alcoholism, juvenile delinquency, and other behaviors that are endemic in society but which at times rise and sweep through the land, constituting sociocultural rather than individual patterns.

When psychiatric recommendations in these matters require changes in the procedures of courts, police, prisons and centers for treatment, then they come in contact with the ways and means for altering laws—with legislation.

MILITARY PSYCHIATRY

This too is an activity of long standing. It goes back at least as far as World War I, which is considerable history for a field as young as psychiatry. Military Psychiatry has as corner stones treatment on the one hand and screening on the other. It then fans out into many dimensions such as separation from service, court-martial, the prevention of breakdown in combat or as a prisoner, the promotion of morale, the interrogation of prisoners of war, psychological warfare, and much else.

. EDUCATIONAL PSYCHIATRY

By this is meant the application of psychiatry to schools, colleges and universities. Let us take the university psychiatrist as the prototype. He, together with his staff, not only sees the student who needs help, but also from time to time provides advice to the administration and either directly or indirectly participates in teaching concerned with student mental health.

INDUSTRIAL PSYCHIATRY

Here a still different range of institutions may be noted and compared with schools and universities on the one hand, and with military units on the other. Industries are social systems with a focus on economic enterprise permeated with such sentiments as the importance of profit, fair wages, competition, efficiency, struggles for power and prestige, group loyalty, worker health and worker morale. A number of psychiatrists have been active in trying to treat mental disorder at an early stage in the plant, and by this means prevent the development of more serious illness. From such a base they have also entered into mental health education and into problems of human relations.

GOVERNMENT PSYCHIATRY

This may be at a municipal, state, or federal level, and as multiphasic as these different collections of human behavior suggest. It can include advising the Commissioner of Parks on recreational facilities, city planners on housing, or trying to answer such questions as, How do we select and maintain healthy, balanced personalities in our offices in foreign countries, particularly those that are isolated so far as the home culture is concerned? or, What can we learn from a study of the psychological reactions to disaster that can be applied in Civil Defense?

PSYCHIATRIC INSTITUTIONS CONSIDERED AS SOCIAL SYSTEMS

This is the psychiatric hospital studied from the viewpoint of sociology, anthropology and social psychology. Understanding the nature of these systems, can serve as an aid in altering and managing them in a manner designed to promote therapeutic effectiveness. Such management of the social environment may be either incidental to other forms of therapy, or the main strategy of treatment.

GROUP PSYCHOTHERAPY

As in the previous instance, so here too the endeavor is to harness group processes and bring them into focus on the individual patient in such a manner as to promote an improvement in his mental health. The group in question is as a rule much smaller and more transitory.

COMMUNITY PSYCHIATRY

What I have in mind under this heading is the psychiatric team—usually composed of social worker and psychologist, as well as psychiatrist—which has as its main goal lifting the level of mental health in the community. This generally means emphasis on the treatment of children, and of illness in its early stages, when presumably more severe and chronic disturbances can be prevented. It also means an emphasis on trying to educate people with regard to factors important in mental health, and trying to exert influence indirectly through training or advising parents, teachers, general practitioners, social workers, public health nurses, and clergymen. Many of the programs of mental health associations may be grouped in this category.

These eight activities do not complete the list that can be considered as subsumed by social psychiatry. Even allowing for the fact that a good many items not mentioned could be viewed as nesting in this or that category, there remain still others which would not easily fit. Notable in this connection are topics such as personality and culture, and the epidemiology of psychiatric disorder. These, however, may be regarded as research areas, rather than areas of action and use, and can be taken up later.[1]

CHARACTERISTICS OF SOCIAL PSYCHIATRY

This presentation of the activities which I should like to regard as falling within the field of social psychiatry is ostensive. The items have been paraded before you as a demonstration of what I have in mind when I speak of social psychiatry, its actions and uses. Such is not a definition, obviously, but a pointing out of examples—much as it would be were I trying to explain what I mean by "animal," and took you to the zoo to show you.

Now, however, the question comes up as to whether or not there are any principles other than whim in terms of which such a collection of activities can be organized in the mind. One negative item has already been mentioned— being different from clinical psychiatry. Are there not some more positive characteristics which could be regarded as common denominators? Are some qualities more expressive of the significance and developmental trend of social psychiatry? After all, difference from clinical psychiatry is not only a negative criterion, but it is also weak. Many things are different from clinical psychiatry such as pearl diving and dog walking. Moreover, it can be said that much of what I have listed amounts to nothing more than clinical psychiatry in particular settings—courts, schools, industry, Army, Navy and so on.

One could argue on the one hand, that there is no

ground for expecting common underlying qualities that have any significance. The various activities mentioned have, for the most part, come into existence independently of each other. Psychiatry and the law, military psychiatry, industrial psychiatry, educational psychiatry, group psychotherapy and the rest have sprung up at different places and at different points in time, and without being knit together by any plan.

On the other hand, it can be maintained that they have a common root in the clinic and that they have in their several ways come into being as a result of needs, of functional gaps in the system which society constitutes. Hence, although there has been no grand strategy, it seems reasonable to suppose that if underlying common features are found, they are probably not entirely accidental nor entirely projections of the observer. It seems likely that they are the product of the interaction of evolving psychiatry and demands arising through changes in society—changes in the direction of increasing size, complexity, and industrialization, of increasing problems of communication, control and standards, and of problems inherent in the disintegrating and regrouping of sociocultural patterns at a rate difficult or impossible for psychological adjustment.

If this is true, then the underlying common features discoverable in the various manifestations of social psychiatry may tell us something about the societal processes in the midst of which we live. Perhaps we can achieve some illumination both with regard to the nature of psychiatry and of the society of which it is a part. From this some ideas may be derived with regard to the future— the recognition of trends that are likely to prevail and grow whether we like them or not, and of opportunities that may be seized, and of potentials waiting to be developed.

With these possibilities in mind, let us look now to see what can be found when the previously mentioned activities of social psychiatry are lined up with an eye to comparison.

1. Social Psychiatry is concerned with people in numbers

Clinical Psychiatry takes each patient at a time, and attempts to mobilize all possible resources to get that person as well as his inner capabilities and outer circumstances will permit. Problems of patients in numbers are not absent, of course, since there are always questions of adequately meeting evident demand. In social psychiatry, however, the matter of numbers is to a greater extent in the foreground, and it has, moreover, implications of enormous importance both as a human problem and as a challenge to the theory and practice of psychiatry. A return to this topic will be made in Part II, page 79-82.

2. Social Psychiatry is concerned with the relationships between mental disorder and sociocultural processes

This is to say that social psychiatry gives attention to some aspect of the regularities and configurations in terms of which human groups function, be they large or small. The participating psychiatrists may have a naive perspective, as is the case in some projects in community psychiatry, or they may launch an ambitious attempt to call on all the resources of the social sciences. In either event, whether naive or sophisticated, there is some kind of involvement with, and recognition of the moulding, directing, containing and changing qualities of sociocultural patterns.

This is obvious, for example, in the case of psychiatry and the courts where psychiatry must fit "the due process of law"—make the most of the system as it occurs, no matter how poorly this may be in consonance with the discoveries and orientation of clinical psychiatry. The judicial procedures, the McNaghten Rule,[2] the laws, the customs and attitudes of the police, the prisons, the various other relevant institutions that exist—and equally those which fail to exist—these are all expressions of one aspect of the functioning of a sociocultural system. They are the on-going sequences of interdependent acts and expectations whereby the society holds itself together in spite of disruptive behavior on the part of individual members.

These patterned sequences of acts and expectations fit together to constitute the system as a whole, somewhat as the functioning of the systems of the body interplay and interdepend to constitute the total person in action. The courts and their procedures as one sub-system within the larger system cannot suspend their actions or change at a word from psychiatry—however right that word might be. Because of their interdependence with so much else, they have to keep functioning, just as breathing and heart beating must go on in a living body if it is to remain a living body. As the surgeon has to adjust to this in his operating, so too must the psychiatrist who works in forensic psychiatry and all that pertains thereto.

Two digressions may be introduced at this point. First, recognizing one's psychiatric activities as taking place within the framework of a system does not mean that one admits alteration to be impossible. As we shall see presently, changing the system may well be one of the most significant potentials in social psychiatry. The point is that this has to be based on appreciation as to the nature of the system, of its many interdependencies and the problem of functioning while undergoing the alteration. The psychiatrist, if he desires change, has to start with things as they are and then construct a series of steps toward his goal.

Psychotherapists will see a parallel here to working with a patient. One must begin at his level and progress by the stages he can tolerate without major disruption of his personality as a functioning system. Nevertheless, it is sometimes observable that the very men and women who are practiced in helpful tolerance of a patient, do not bring this to bear on institutions and communities. Instead they may be critical, accusing, moralistic and uninformed in their attitude toward the social system and its leaders. If this is simply blowing off steam in private conversation over the frustrations experienced in trying to help patients, there is little harm in it. If, however, it is said with serious intent of bringing about constructive change, and particularly if it is a part of public speaking or writing, then one can predict that it is a way of acting which is not likely to have better success with communities than with patients. It may work occasionally when shock is needed, but mostly it builds resistance.

The second digression is to note that clinical psychiatry is also in the toils of the social system. The disorder of the patient is in part a precipitate, if not a product, of the functioning of society, and the range of potentialities for treatment are created and limited by the sociocultural matrix in which both psychiatrist and patient exist. All this is obvious and explicitly recognized by many clinicians. The point being made here, therefore, is one of degree. The social psychiatrist is more rather than less caught up in having to understand the characteristics of the social system, and he is apt to be more active in matters having to do with changing them.

Returning now to the thread of the discourse, it may be noted by way of summary that what has been said about the prominence of the functioning of the social system in the calculations of the social psychiatrist is applicable to all our eight categories: not only to the psychiatrist in the legal context as used for illustration, but also in the military services, in the educational setting, in industry, in government, in the psychiatric hospital viewed as a social system, in group psychotherapy, and in the community.

Let us pause to examine group psychotherapy in a little more detail. Such therapy has, as already noted, a particular emphasis on turning sociocultural processes—particularly small-group processes—into channels that will promote recovery. This is a matter of some interest for, as is well known, the traditional attitude of the psychiatrist is to regard much of sociocultural activity, particularly socialization, as the enemy of his patient, and indirectly of himself. The clinician has been prone to think of the patient as one who has had his illness fostered by the constraints put on his natural urges during infancy and childhood, and by their perpetuation in his adult life so as to keep him a frustrated victim locked in the iron fist of his psychic mechanisms.

Setting the origins of disorder aside for the time being, it is certain that the patient *is* often misunderstood by others, and that the sentiments[3] of these others can present a wall around him that impedes recovery. In group psychotherapy, however, the outlook is reversed and the sentiments of others, the collective others of the particular group, are put to work in supporting the patient in his evolution toward a healthier inter- and intra-personal patterning of existence. This use of societal influences is largely an invention by psychiatry, the creation of a sociocultural pattern that can function in the service of treatment.[4]

When the psychiatric hospital is viewed as a social institution, something similar is possible; the functioning of this system can be altered so as to improve the therapeutic effect. More is meant by this than the mere removal of obstacles to psychotherapy; rather it is a question of something active in its own right: the guiding of the group processes so that they draw the patient into some of the normal roles an individual can have in his society, so they support the concomitant intrapsychic changes. Societal influences have great capacity of determination, and the goal is to have them working for, rather than against, the patient.

If the idea of the constructive use of sociocultural patterns is enlarged to include not only therapy, but also under certain circumstances diagnosis, appropriate disposition, arrangements whereby patients can live in communities rather than in hospitals, care after hospital discharge, and prophylaxis, then it stands as a component in some degree of almost all the activities that can be considered as instances of social psychiatry. In short, a characteristic of social psychiatry is not only the explicit recognition of, and adjustment to sociocultural patterns, not only the alteration of those that are undesirable from the psychiatric point of view, but also the constructive and creative use of these patterns in the services of diagnosis, treatment and prevention.

My third point is a related theme, but has to do with the value-sentiments of psychiatrist and society, rather than society conceived as a functional system. It is more ethical than scientific in its orientation.

3. Social Psychiatry has responsibility to a society, or a subgroup within a society, and this takes precedence over obligations to the patient

An unequivocal example can be seen in military psychiatry. The acceptance of this situation has sometimes been difficult for psychiatrists who have gone from private and clinical pactice into the armed services and who had up till then been accustomed to think of their obligations purely in terms of the patient. There can be no doubt, however, that in the Army, the Navy and Air Force, the welfare of the unit must come before the welfare of any individual patient. The closer one is to combat, the more stark this is, and the psychiatrist has to think not only of how to help the boy before him, but also all the other boys in the same outfit. His actions on behalf of one must be within a framework of calculations for the many. This includes those who are not ill now, but may become so later, and also those who will, in all likelihood, never become ill.

There is, moreover, a consideration even beyond the welfare of the group. This is the purpose for which the group exists—winning the war and so protecting, at whatever sacrifice of individuals, the larger society of which they are a part.

These responsibilities are not diffuse, but mediated by a clear-cut hierarchy of authority. The psychiatrist has limited freedom for interpreting the principles in particular cases, and must, to a large extent, act according to rules set down for him, and on orders issued by superiors.

The military situation has been taken as an extreme example, one in which the point is most evident. In subtler —and hence perhaps more confusing and perplexing terms —the matter of obligation to a group, an institution, or a society before obligation to a patient, obtains in most other activities within the borders of social psychiatry.

In court, the clinician is under the influence of a concept of justice, which means he has a sense of duty to some image of humanity as a collectivity, of doing something not only for this particular individual on trial, but for all other individuals as well. This general allegiance to a human group is given a specific form through the psychiatrist being retained by the defense, or the prosecution; or, in some more fortunate cases, being retained by the court.

With industrial psychiatry, the superordinate responsibility is to the workers of a company or plant. There is also, however, the matter of the business success. As in the case of the military, what the psychiatrist does is carried out within a framework of authority; he is responsible to the management or the union. The latter relationship is, unfortunately, as yet rare. Perhaps someday a system will be evolved whereby members of our profession can be responsible to some kind of joint board on which management and labor are both represented.

In educational institutions, the obligation is to the administration on behalf of the student. The case is similar with governments where officials act on behalf of the citizenry.

In community psychiatry, obligation may be at its most diffuse. Basically and ideally, it is to the community as a whole and to the nation, but practically this comes down to some compound of government agencies, contributing charitable and welfare organizations, and influential community leaders. This diffusion is sometimes an advantage in giving the clinical team more autonomy, but it can also result in having to live amid a continual stream of influential requests and in being fought over like a bone.

In psychiatric institutions and especially in group psychotherapy, the responsibility of the psychiatrist to a group more than to a patient may be played down, but not entirely. If the group is to stay a group, it must take precedence over any particular individual.

In making these points I do not wish to imply that there is a continuing state of conflict. For the most part, the obligations of the psychiatrist to a social unit, its aims and its authority, are not in conflict with his duties to particular patients. Indeed, the group itself—including the military—has generally a set of value-sentiments that give a reasonable place to the individual, his needs and his rights. Nevertheless, the possibility of conflict always exists, and becomes critically, painfully manifest in actual situations from time to time.

It is not pleasant to contemplate putting a patient's requirements in a subordinate position. To do so flies in the face of man's reaching and struggling to make real his visions of what human life could be. This is something more than the age-old and often dramatized conflicts of human motivation. The clash between loyalties, between "I would" and "I ought," and between honor and desire have preoccupied minds through the centuries and in many civilizations, as reflected in Antigone, in Hamlet and in Chushingura, the story of the forty-seven Ronin.

What is modern is a sense of the importance of every individual, not just kings, nobility and special classes of free citizens, his right to certain freedoms, his right to opportunity for self-development. The dawn of the Christian era gave importance to the individual soul, the Rennaissance to the individual mind, and the late eighteenth century to the individual. Clinical psychiatry has long been the champion of the individual, and has had a large and pervasive influence in modern times, meeting and re-inforcing similar trends in the arts, in literature, in law, in philosophy, in political thinking and in religion. While this championship may have had its origin in revolt against the bindings imposed by certain aspects of Victorian life, it has certainly matured into something positive and joined with other trends of civilization.

Social psychiatry is not to be considered as taking a course against these trends, but it is probably correct to say that the position of the social psychiatrist in relation to such matters is somewhat different from that of his colleague doing therapy. The latter has a privileged and unusual position. This is part of the larger pattern of doctor-patient relationship characteristic of our culture. The aspect that is unusual and privileged is the degree to which the physician is free to put the individual's welfare above almost every consideration. Few other client-oriented relationships in our culture at present go this far, although traditionally the clergyman saving souls surpassed it. The sick man, woman, or child and his doctor are given an especially protected niche. It may be a question how long this pattern will continue, in view of the march of events, but thus far we still have it. The activities of social psychiatry, it seems, enmesh the participants more immediately in some of the pangs and thrusts of social change and in responses to widespread human needs.

At this point I should like to pause again from sketching the characteristics of social psychiatry and suggest that the time is at hand for reassessment of some of the premises on which psychiatric sentiments about group and individual are based, and then a working out of orientation and policy for dealing with situations as they emerge. There could be greater clarity regarding what we stand for, and some explicit recognition of the direction in which we should like to go. As it is, we are apt to vacillate, drifting from one *ad hoc* decision to another. In a somewhat muddled way, many issues such as political liberalism and conservatism, academic freedom, free-enterprise, laissez faire economy, socialized medicine, manipulating people for their own good and much else bubbles through these moments of decision. Sometimes the considerations are wholly irrelevant to the issue, but get triggered by words or acts that have symbolic connotations, almost clang associations. In other instances there is relevancy, but its nature is obscured by the emotions stirred like heat waves between an observer and a distant object.

The fact that it is unpleasant to contemplate the rights and needs of the individual as eclipsed by societal demands, tempts one to look the other way, or to huddle closer into the doctor-patient dyad. It can also lead to making over-simplified definitions of the problem, and to taking embattled positions. Such escapes are dangerous because the problem is fundamental and is on our backs, to stay and grow until some solution is found—blind or intelligent, constructive or destructive. It is one of the really great problems of our time and belongs in a class with the question of man's ability to survive his nuclear discoveries. It runs to the heart of the unrest that could trigger a terminal war, and it runs to the heart of the question whether a way of life designed to achieve survival will be a way of life that is worth having.

Let me hasten to say here that I am not, with these remarks, claiming a psychiatric monopoly in the matter. I am not placing psychiatry in front of the nuclear age, as in front of a rising sun, to give it a long shadow. It is rather that psychiatry in common with many other human activities, has a share in the problem and has particular questions that are its own.

How widespread the root problem is, can be seen from the fact that a comparative study of sociocultural change at different points on the earth's surface shows mankind as marching in at least two opposite directions at once.[5] On the one hand, with urbanization, nationalization, technological change, and corporative and cooperative development, there is progressive loss of individual and small group autonomy. Health, education, industrial and agricultural productivity are improving the world over. Enormous advances are still necessary, but the trend is there.

Yet, as this happens the power of decision and independence of choice at the local level is progressively eroded. In our own countryside, a century ago local boards of village and town took care of welfare, sanitation, roads, schools and much else. Perhaps they did so very badly by modern standards, but at least they had the responsibility, freedom of choice and self-determination. Today, those activities are largely out of local hands. They are much more professional, with higher quality and more effectiveness, but most of the decisions that matter are made at a distance, by people not directly affected and the activities are less rather than more under individual and community control. In many instances we cannot even understand the problems that affect us most vitally, or have the information in terms of which these decisions by others are made.

Perhaps the predicament is symbolized by the turnpikes and throughways which reach across the country impelled by the traffic mass, and probably military considerations, but certainly without regard to the wishes of the people in each farm, village and small town along the way. The paradox is that while this is happening, ideas of individual freedom of choice are expanding, not only as ideas, but through society, so that more people of all kinds the world over feel more deeply the rights and dignity of the individual as something that must be realized.

The paradox is compounded when, in order to express these rising needs, people submit to regimentation in military services, in unions, in professional societies, and other organizations, each with attendant group loyalties and suppression of the individual for the common goals.

I mention these large and far-flung matters only to indicate that social psychiatry has a bite on something vastly more extensive than its own field of action. There is, however, the chance that in coming to grips with the particular manifestations in its area of competence, psychiatry could make a useful demonstration of one way in which such vexing problems can be tackled. This possibility is at least a test of psychiatric knowledge and insight regarding human behavior.

4. Social Psychiatry is concerned with conducting knowledge out of the clinic into various strategic places in the sociocultural system

This might be called the "pipe-line leading out."

At their beginning, activities in social psychiatry such as in the Army, industry and the rest, are apt to be, in essence, clinical psychiatry in a particular setting. You will recall my noting earlier that some people might regard the illustrations given as being no more than this. It is appropriate now to point to some of the extensions and new forms that are developing.

Industry can be selected as an example. Psychiatry is not yet widespread in this field, and in most instances it has come into existence as part of the medical division in a plant. As such it has to do mainly with psychological emergencies that occur during working hours. Chronic illnesses requiring long treatment are not generally the province of the industrial psychiatrist. From the emergency vantage point, however, from being the person to whom those in emotional trouble go, the psychiatrist can soon become concerned with the interpersonal situations in the plant that precipitate such events. He can begin to define chronic and recurrent sources of difficulty as lying in the patterns according to which the plant functions as a social system. When these are put together with his general clinical knowledge of factors bearing on the origin, course and outcome of psychiatric disorders, he is in a position to advise management regarding changes in the system that could make it healthier from the psychiatric point of view. He is also in a position to conduct educational sessions for various levels of management, and for the workers. It is this kind of thing that I have in mind when I speak of piping the lore of clinical psychiatry into a social system.

It should be noted at once, however, that in reaching the areas of industry where it can take effect, the psychiatric stream mingles with many other streams that are flowing in the same direction. By these "other streams" I refer to various of the applied social sciences, particularly those grouped under the heading of "Human Relations." This usually comprises some mixture of sociology, psychology, social psychology and cultural anthropology. The psychiatrist has the task of taking his place along with representatives of these fields in striving toward better systems of human relations in the work situation. "Better" is of course, likely to have a number of different definitions among these several disciplines, but it generally includes some common ground of ideas about happiness, freedom from annoyance, improved productivity and stability of the working force.[6]

The psychiatrist soon finds—occasionally to his surprise —that he is not an expert in all areas of human relationships. He discovers that the several varieties of social scientists have useful perceptions and types of knowledge about human beings which he does not possess, and so too do many of the practical operators in human affairs, the members of management and the leaders in unions. For any one type of individual or discipline, such knowledge and insight is apt to be spotty, and each is prone to make what members of another discipline can point to as bad mistakes. The psychiatrist has to admit that he is in this class too, that he is sometimes ignorant and blundering in his ideas about how interpersonal relations should be managed and that knowledge of psychopathology is not always a useful framework for interpreting human relations. This can have the useful effect of throwing him back into taking stock and asking himself just what it is he has to contribute. Setting professional rivalries aside, and the natural desire to see one's own group as having the highest degree of excellence—the most vital contribution to make—just what can a psychiatrist bring to improving human relations that other behavioral sciences do not bring?

The answer to this contains at least three important items. One is that the psychiatrist can differentiate the pathological as distinct from the merely disagreeable. He can as a professional recognize psychiatric disorder and he has some idea of the circumstances apt to be associated with it. One of his basic contributions is, then, despite what was said above, from knowledge of pathology.

Some of my colleagues will disagree with me here, and say that psychiatry is no longer limited to pathology; on the contrary, its goal and orientation is in terms of positive mental health. I have no quarrel with this as an aspiration, but I have grave doubts that our actual knowledge and experience in this matter is commensurate with our knowledge and experience of pathology. Furthermore, many other disciplines besides ourselves have competencies bearing on health, while psychopathology is our forte.[7]

A second item is the psychiatrist's insights and knowledge with regard to human motivation. This is based on the idea that pathology offers one kind of window into the processes of personality, and that what is learned through this window has wider application than in instances of disorder. Ideas derived from illness must, of course, be interpreted with caution when used as a framework for gauging the apparently normal. The point remains, nonetheless, that this is an area of experience from which the psychiatrist can draw. I should like to emphasize that it *is experience* and *with people*, not based only on reading, theory, or limited laboratory tests; and it is experience with a wide variety of persons in connection with whom the ideas of motivation have been put to a trial of workability in therapy.

The third item is the psychiatrist's training and familiarity with considering human beings as wholes—a regard for the total blending of organic, psychological and sociocultural factors. This is a glib thing to say, and it is easily passed off as a statement that is both obvious and at the same time more or less without substance. And yet the vast majority of diagnostic and therapeutic efforts are practical attempts at taking into account the many aspects of personality, and conceiving them in some kind of synthesis.

In pointing to these three items—knowledge of pathology, insight into human motivation, and experience in dealing with personality as a whole—I must admit that psychiatrists do not always make a very good showing. Some of us will have a narrow view of motives and consider one set to the exclusion of all others; and some will show acquaintance with a limited aspect of personality and make all interpretations within such a framework. Nevertheless, psychiatry as a discipline does provide training and experience with regard to these three items and many psychiatrists have made the most of the opportunity; and no other discipline does supply just this. They supply other experiences, of course, and I am not comparing disciplines in terms of intrinsic worth, but rather trying to state the type of contribution most pertinent from psychiatry—some of the kinds of knowledge and experience psychiatry can siphon out of the clinic and pipe into the sociocultural system.

With military, educational and community psychiatry the opportunity is similar to that in industrial psychiatry. On some occasions this may be quite highly developed, while in others it may not. Community psychiatry can be taken as an example that presents the whole range. In some situations it is nothing more than clinical psychiatry in a community context, with some pressure to treat disorder early and dispose of it quickly so that a large volume can be handled. At the other extreme is the clinical team that spends a great deal of time on educational programs, and which works with patients indirectly through consultation and advice to general practitioners, teachers, clergy and parent groups. It may also have influence that reaches into legislation.

The courts begin as a rule with only one aspect of clinical psychiatry—diagnosis and appraisal. From problems of particular cases, however, there is evolution into problems of how cases should be handled, leading to attempts to influence judicial procedures and ultimately the law itself. The teaching of psychiatry has become a part of the curriculum in a number of law schools.[8]

To sum up, then, the lore of clinical psychiatry is piped by the activities of social psychiatry into the sociocultural system at such points of apparent need as the courts, the penal system, the legislature, educational institutions, human relations in industry, general medicine and pastoral work.[9]

It must be granted that the ways and means of doing all this are neither apparent nor easy, and hence a developing branch of social psychiatry is one concerned with the definition of just such aims and the establishment of means and techniques for their accomplishment. This is a field of specialization in itself, one which can be considered as distinctive of social psychiatry as compared to clinical psychiatry.

5. Social Psychiatry is concerned with conducting relevant knowledge into the field of clinical psychiatry

This is the converse of the previous, a "pipe-line leading in," instead of out.

Through its own experiences and research discoveries and through its contact with the social sciences, social psychiatry is in a position to select and transmit into the stream of clinical psychiatry such information, orientation, insights and methods, as may be appropriate for aiding in diagnosis and treatment. What this can amount to is not, perhaps, too clear at the present time and yet one can point to the analyses of psychiatric institutions as

social systems, and the development of group psychotherapy as activities capable of direct impact on thinking and practice with regard to the treatment of the individual. Studies of personality and culture, done mainly
within the framework of anthropology, have certainly had
an influence on many therapists, and the same may well
be, or prove true, of studies of the dynamic characteristics
of small groups carried on in social psychology, of communication studies, of surveys of opinion and attitude
according to sociological groupings, and of psychological
experiments in such fields as conditioning and ethology.[10]

It is apparent as one mentions these fields that they
often reach the minds of clinicians without being mediated through social psychiatry. While it is desirable that
this should be so and no empire for social psychiatry is
proposed, this may not be enough. There remains the
likelihood that many of those engaged in clinical work
will never hear of items that would be useful to them,
simply because these other fields are so extensive and
the clinician has not time to read widely. Or, if the clinician does attempt it, he may find himself baffled by the
several technical languages and the difficulty of taking
out what is actually relevant to his interests. It would
seem, therefore, that because social psychiatry has a root
in the clinic and an awareness of what the clinical practitioner needs, it can emphasize the selection, synthesis
and interpretation of the relevant. This does go on at
present, but it could be regarded as an area inviting much
more development.

In this connection, it may be noted that the social psychiatrist has several audiences: in addition to the clinical
psychiatrist, there are his colleagues in social psychiatry

itself, people in other behavioral sciences, and the men and women playing active parts in the functioning and changing of society such as legislators, administrators, educators, lawyers and the clergy.

Five items have been reviewed as characteristic of social psychiatry: dealing with patients in numbers, attention to sociocultural processes, a sense of primary responsibility to a group, carrying the fruits of clinical knowledge into the social system, and conducting results from other behavorial sciences into clinical psychiatry. I should like to suggest that these five characteristics consitute a syndrome. By this is meant that if one were trying to decide whether a given activity is to be considered social psychiatry, we do not have to insist that all of these characteristics be evident, but only that there be a preponderance. There are no hard and fast lines between social psychiatry and numbers of other approaching activities, including clinical psychiatry. It may nevertheless be useful to think that the more an activity exhibits these five qualities, the more it is appropriate to regard it as social psychiatry, and to consider these five as, all together, a set of related functional needs, characteristic of our society at the present time—needs that have many discrete manifestations, and needs which are changing in quality and intensity as we speak of them.[11]

SOME LINES FOR DEVELOPMENT

To some extent, the potentialities of social psychiatry for action and use, are obvious in what has been said. It can become more of what it is already. There are reaches open along lines presently evident in the law, in the armed forces, in education, in industry, in government, in the community, in the study of psychiatric institutions as social systems, and in group psychotherapy. There remain, however, a number of opportunities for development that are not already well launched or even clearly defined. Some pertain to situations that are waiting, while others are matters of anticipating the trend of events in society, in civilization.

A first point then is that of tackling more squarely the problem of prevention. Educational psychiatry, industrial psychiatry and community psychiatry are mainly oriented in terms of therapy. What I am suggesting is that the model provided by public health be taken more seriously. Prevention should be conceived not just as early treatment, but as reducing the frequency of first occurrence, of scotching the trouble before it starts.

I anticipate here a quick challenge with the question: how? And I submit to the magnitude and seriousness of the difficulties implied by the asking. To a large extent the answer must be that research is needed, and this matter will be taken up presently in Part II. But such is not the whole story, for despite the limited character of our knowledge, we know more than we practice. Maternal and child health care, the control of physical hazards in the environment, and the prevention of malnutrition are examples of action spheres that bear on the occurrence of certain psychiatric disorders that have an organic basis. Almost equally clear is the relationship of chronic emotional strain to psychophysiological illness such as peptic ulcer, coronary disease and asthma. Saying this does not, of course, imply thinking in terms of a single cause, but rather that environmentally induced emotional strain is one of the critical factors among those responsible for the appearance of disorder.

The picture is probably similar with regard to many types of psychoneurotic, psychotic and other symptoms particularly as concerns the development and precipitation of severe impairment of the person's functioning. While evidence on this point is neither so precise nor so systematic as could be wished, the general mass of impression from many, many different sources is so overwhelming that one is inclined to feel that the burden of proof is on him who would deny it. The evidence as to the damaging effect of situations producing chronic emotional strain certainly seems enough to warrant trying to reduce their occurrence.

The fact that we do not understand the exact nature of the etiological components is not necessarily a reason for delaying action. Public health experience shows that it is at times worthwhile to attempt environmental controls when an association has been demonstrated even before the reasons are fully understood. Cholera provides a well known illustration of this, inasmuch as the relationship of certain water supplies to the disease was found, and control demonstrated as possible, before recognition of the *Vibrio cholerae*.[12]

The blocks to applying what we know, or hold as a reasonable assumption, are often matters of sentiment, custom and practical difficulties which interfere with altering the relevant segments of the sociocultural system. For instance, in psychiatry as in medicine, most physicians are far more interested in treating individuals than in treating communities, factories or educational institutions. Philosophically, we are all in favor of prevention, but as a matter of professional life most of us prefer to spend our time helping those who are ill and to leave prevention to someone else. One result of this is that we do not have a widely understood and accepted concept of prevention. Instead the word, like the older words "mental hygiene" tends to be used to cover a somewhat loose set of ideas about early treatment, child psychiatry and the avoidance of recurrence. Furthermore, to the extent it is genuinely a preventive and not a therapeutic idea, it has to do with the adaptation of individuals, rather than the removing of noxious complexes from society.[13]

Another point is the psychiatrist's unfamiliarity with dealing in sociocultural problems and sociocultural processes. By this I do not refer to basic gaps in human knowledge in these areas—of which there are of course plenty. What I have in mind is knowledge which does exist but is in such fields as applied anthropology, sociology and psychology. The problem here, therefore, is not one of discovery, but of bringing into conjunction several relevant streams of experience, skill and information.

Much of what the psychiatrist lacks he can obtain through the help of persons trained in these relevant social sciences.

Aside from the psychiatrist's inclinations, there is the problem of the surrounding attitudes of administrators, policy makers, workers, students, political leaders, and the public generally. Here it is not just a question of understanding, but of willingness to cope with changes which, if put into action, would certainly have far reaching effects—and some of them disturbing—on many of the current patterns of our existence. Inherent in this are problems of competing goals, the value of mental health in relation to other desirables. *Post partum* psychoses could be eradicated by doing away with pregnancy for instance, but plainly our values are such that this would be the greater evil. There are other propositions of this type, however, in which the answer is not so obvious. How much, for instance, should the profits of an industry be reduced supposing this were necessary in order to improve the mental health of the workers? How much are people willing to be taxed for the sake of lessening psychiatric disorder? And how should a tax of this kind be rated in comparison to taxes to support education and maintain roads?

I should like to suggest that there would be merit in developing social psychiatry teams that could take the factory, the community, the university, the government agency or other similar organization, as the focal point of attention. Such a focal point could be subjected to diagnosis in terms of identifying within its total system those patterns which are fostering psychiatric disorder among the constituent members—unhealthy patterns. Following this diagnosis, there could then be the working out of plans for remedy in collaboration with all those who are bound up in the matter, both administrating and administered. In teams capable of this functioning, one could see blended, the skills of psychiatry, sociology, anthropology, social psychology and statistics in much the same way one sees medicine, bacteriology, nutrition, nursing, statistics and other fields tied together in public health work.

Looking still further ahead, one could anticipate that the functioning of such teams would be mainly in problem situations. Diagnosis and the institution of remedy might be the limit of their attention to any one organization or community. The problem of maintaining the remedy might well be taken over by others. That is to say, it may not require the attention of a psychiatrist once the goals and program have been established. Professionals in the field of human relations could probably carry this on as members of a management staff, or as advisors to the administration of a community.

Industry, it seems to me, offers a particular opportunity for making a start in the development of teams concerned with raising the level of mental health by means of prevention. This does not mean it would be easy, but the organization and functioning of many industries is such that once the idea had been worked out, it would stand a chance of acceptance by unions and by management. Activities somewhat after this pattern are already in existence, oriented in terms of the more general viewpoint of improving human relations. Some large companies have teams that go from one branch to another assessing the appropriateness of the organization to the social and psychological characteristics of its people. There are also independent firms which provide evaluative services for hire.[14] In few if any of these, however, is there psychiatric participation with contributions from the three sources I mentioned earlier: understanding of psychopathology, human motivation and personality as a whole. Nowhere in industry, so far as I know, does a preventive team of the type I have sketched, occur. This is a large opening which psychiatry has not perceived, much less seized. I feel this is so important and so much a central point in the action and uses of social psychiatry, that I am tempted to say that, as exemplars of social psychiatry, neither industrial psychiatry nor community psychiatry as yet really exist.

A second potential for the evolution of social psychiatry is in underdeveloped areas, an aspect of the problem of international relations. All over the world, peoples are undergoing industrialization, and acquiring modern methods of agriculture and medicine, including public health. To a large extent, this movement is being guided by experts in the relevant technical fields. That there are human problems of vast proportions in the socio-cultural changes which go with the technological development, is recognized by those engaged in such work, but only somewhat and inadequately. It is fully realized, however, in the social sciences and many workers trained in those disciplines, especially anthropology, are turning their skills toward helping the technologist and the administrator humanize the process of change. The problem is to introduce the benefits without producing secondary effects that can be so disastrous in their consequences as to raise the question whether the benefits are worth their cost.

Psychiatry enters the picture because rapid sociocultural change can be pathogenic. As noted before, this is not a fact established on a scientific basis, but it is a conclusion reached from a wide variety of observations and one which is sufficiently probable to warrant action on the presumption that it is generally, if not inevitably, true. It warrants the employment of social psychiatry as among the disciplines contributing ways and means for humanizing change. Here again, the contribution would stem from the knowledge of psychopathology, of human motivation, and of human beings considered as whole personalities. I would not, however, visualize in this instance such a definitely structured team as in the case of diagnosing and treating the mental health problems of industry, or communities. It would not, in fact, be a social psychiatry team, but rather a behavioral science team with social psychiatry as one of the important contributors. While there has been a little of this already, by and large it is an opening as yet unfilled.[15] It presents for psychiatry a major problem toward the solution of which we can make a contribution, as we familiarize ourselves with its nature, as we assess the lore and methods of our own field in relation to it, and as we learn to work with the other behavorial sciences.

The matter of change in human life which flags our attention in the underdeveloped areas turns out on closer inspection to be a variant of a larger problem, and one that is so close to home, as to be in the house. We ourselves are impelled and bewildered by change as much as those who live in underdeveloped areas. Ever since the beginning of the industrial revolution, the history of the West has been a history of change. This has not been circular or rhythmical from one more or less familiar pattern to another. Rather, it has been spiral, always bringing forth the unknown, always threatening the present with a future that will make it obsolete. This is more than cars or gadgets; it is a matter of values, information, orientation,—all the dimensions of the mind that give life meaning, and the potential for satisfaction or despair. Furthermore, not only is it change piled on change in bewildering sequence, but it is change with acceleration.

This motion is fraught with potentials for good and evil to the human race. From the long point of view, I do not wish to stress the one of these over the other. In the immediate, however, the acceleration is a serious matter. If change can be pathogenic for the members of under-developed areas, it is no less so for us, and we have ourselves to look to in this regard. Automation and the use of atomic energy will probably not introduce any problems we do not already have in kind, but they may create new levels of both extensiveness and acceleration in regard to such matters as technological unemployment, leisure time for which people are unprepared, and the danger of vast power in the hands of a few. Promethus, Pandora's box, the Sorceror's Apprentice, Faust—these myths of European man suggest early recognition of questions still unsolved, but ever more pressing.

In addition to the problem of accelerated change *per se,* the sky of the times we live in is, of course, overcast by a number of epochal new sources of fear. There is for some of us, something elementally terrifying about hitting the moon with rockets and beginning to monkey with the workings of the solar system. It becomes literally true that you do not know what to expect next, and "next" is any moment, not next month or next year. The framework of stability crumbles for many people and we are then apt to shy like a horse at what is only a bit of white paper blowing in the wind.

More immediate and real—and yet so unreal that its reality escapes one's grasp—is the threat of nuclear war, and the unprecedented problems of living in a state of extreme preparedness without fighting. If the real meaning of civil defence is ever put into practice and we seriously consider living so that a reasonable proportion of the national population could survive a nuclear and biological attack, then it is not an exaggeration to say we have not as yet discovered what change is.

This threat of destruction, in addition to accelerated change, is something to regard as also pathogenic, as damaging to mental health. And, if it fosters psychiatric disorder, this is at one level serious, just as it would be if it fostered bubonic plague.

But at another level it is still more serious. One of the central features of most types of psychiatric disorder is a sequence in which an intolerable state of emotions leads to acts that produce some relief, some discharge often based on manipulation of symbols. Such acts can be suicidal as when the Assembly of Athens went into a rage and condemned to death without hearing the evidence eight of their generals who were in fact heros of a battle off the Arginusae Islands and vitally needed in the struggle with Sparta. Similar acts by tyrants of the ancient world are even more numerous. And you can trace patterns to the present, through the mobs of the French revolution and men of power like Robespierre, down to the obvious examples in modern times.

These we cannot now afford. We cannot afford mobs bent on catharsis, nor dictators attempting compensation for personality defect at the expense of the world. We may not be able to avoid these age-old surgings of a non-rational character, extending through too much power. Yet, it is worth the try, for if we do not find a method to help man deal constructively with his changing, his uncertainties, his anxieties, his hostilities, and his life in a state of suspended threat, then one of his emotional-symbol acts may well be the farewell gesture of humanity.

The obvious relevance of motivation and the processes of psychopathology to all of this suggests a place for social psychiatry in the try. But, accepting this, there is the matter of where to take hold. The problems are everywhere, yet apparently nowhere firmly graspable. This very permeation suggests that we can begin with what is nearest. If accelerated change and the problem of living in a threatened world saturate everything, then social psychiatry can begin to deal with these at the points where it is now working in the courts, in the reformation of laws, in educational institutions, in industry, in government and in community. Numbers of roads stand open along which to make multiple and, ultimately, converging attempts.

Part II

THE WIDENING OF KNOWLEDGE

INTRODUCTION

Let me begin what will be a discussion of research by recalling from Part I that social psychiatry may be regarded as a syndrome with five main concerns: people in numbers, sociocultural processes, obligations to a group, conducting knowledge from clinical psychiatry to apposite places in the sociocultural system, and conducting knowledge from the behavioral sciences into clinical psychiatry. These characteristics have been selected for attention as a result of considering a number of psychiatric activities carried out as services to mankind. In turning to research we can anticipate that it will be to some degree within the same framework, constitute an adjunct to actions and uses. It is therefore appropriate to look first at this aspect of the matter.

APPLIED RESEARCH

The aim in such work is to make discoveries that will enable one to pursue more effectively the goals now seen. By what steps can the law be brought into closer harmony with what is known of psychiatric disorder? What can be substituted for the McNaghten Rule? How can selection for military service, and other special tasks, screen out those with disorders that render them unsuitable? What concepts, methods and techniques are appropriate for teams concerned with identifying noxious sociocultural patterns in communities, plants, government agencies and other human organizations? How can things be ordered so that people may move into places in the social system where they can realize their potential abilities and experience fulfillment? How can remedial measures be developed which are consonant both with the requirements of mental health and the ongoing functional needs of the society or subunit of the society? How can the problems of communication between psychiatrists and other behavioral scientists be solved, and between both of these and policy makers, managers, leaders, and various segments of the public? What are the methods with which to conduct mental health education so that there is an effect that is both desirable and lasting? How can mental hospitals be reorganized so as to make the environment they offer more therapeutic? Can the theories and techniques of small group studies be applied effectively in group psychotherapy? Can change in severity and frequency of psychiatric disorder in populations be accurately measured so as to permit a testing of results obtained by the various activities concerned with improving the level of mental health, whether it be in small groups, hospitals, or samples of populations in their natural settings? Perhaps most important of all, how do we find the best way to bring the resources of psychiatry to bear on the current stresses of society, whether developed or underdeveloped, and how do we select out of psychiatry's cupboard those items best suited to these purposes?

These are but a few of the questions of pragmatic and operative character that confront the advance of social psychiatry as an applied field of endeavor. I mention them as examples and to indicate an order of problem, so as to register them as an area of importance, and then pass on to other kinds of problems—those that may be labeled as basic research.

BASIC RESEARCH -
SOME UNDERLYING ASSUMPTIONS

In coming now to basic research, the focal point of attention is extended to matters not hitherto directly considered. We move from action and use to the question of widening fundamental knowledge, and social psychiatry comes in this aspect to partake of the main characteristics of all such endeavors. There is thus a further development in a scientific framework of the "syndrome," with particular reference to those divisions noted earlier as concerned with people in numbers and with sociocultural processes.

"Basic" is one of those words that is overloaded with its own importance. Like "dynamic" it has more than a hint of polite abuse about it, as would be evident if I were to say, "Your theories are not basic." When I emphasize "basic" here, it is not to confer knighthood on a set of problems, but only to indicate characteristics. I do not mean to claim more—or less—importance for them as compared to applied research.

The central point in basic research is etiology, the problem of cause in psychiatric disorder, and especially cause in mental health.

Cause as an idea, that is casualty, is an exceedingly perplexing concept as soon as one begins to push the matter toward some definite and fundamental framework of meaning. It becomes very difficult to avoid both paradox and tautology and the problem is of a piece with the question of understanding time, space and motion when considered beyond the limits of the earth, out in the universe. Certain working assumptions, however, involving time and space and applicable to the world, are a common basis of most sciences and we may therefore begin at this level. One such working concept holds that any event in nature is the product of other antecedent events.

This may seem self-evident, and yet it is only an assumption. As I understand it, Hume was the first in modern times to call the matter in question. He believed that you could demonstrate that certain events were caused by other events, but he denied any basis except faith for assuming casualty as a general principal of the universe. Kant took this further and proposed the exceedingly plausible idea that casual relationships are characteristic of human thinking rather than of nature, it is a way we have of ordering the events which impinge upon our senses. The matter of correspondence between this ordering and reality is unknown.[16]

To illustrate this, consider the origin of the universe. With one thought we hold that some set of conditions must have caused it, but with the next we hold that some other set of conditions must in turn have caused the first. That is, if conditions X produced the universe, then conditions Y must have produced X, and so X is not really the cause of the universe, but rather Y. Yet, again back of Y, there must be Z and so on, and on. All this arises as an insoluble problem because of an assumption characteristic of the human mind: there must be a cause of the universe; it must have had a beginning and something must have started it.

If on the other hand we suppose the universe always existed, that is to say, is causeless, these problems disappear. But while it is easy to say the universe has always existed and hence has no original set of causes, this is a proposition that is almost, if not entirely, impossible for the mind to grasp.

It may be noted in passing that religious thinkers have dealt with this set of problems by taking God as the causeless first cause. Reason is recognized as a human attribute and hence also its limits, and faith is introduced as the guiding star for the seas that surround and extend beyond reason. Locke is perhaps a good example of this kind of thinking. As is well known, he compared the mind to a sailor's sounding line of limited length which would reach some depths, but not all those of the ocean.

Within the framework of scientific research, however, we must take as a fundamental assumption that any event upon which we focus our attention is the product of other events, is enmeshed in streams of causal factors which it is our task to elucidate. This elucidation can be cast in terms of two somewhat different frames of reference. One of these may be called "historical causation," and is exemplified in the way the characteristics of animal species today are explained by evolutionary sequences. It is also characteristic of the way a psychiatrist thinks of a neurotic disorder as the product of a patient's life story.

The other may be called "systematic causation" following Kurt Lewin and refers to the position of an element in a system.[17] We are thinking in this frame of reference when we regard the sun and moon as causing the tides, or of a body falling because of gravity. Both viewpoints are, of course, useful in explanatory systems. It may be that some of the existentialists are bringing the second one to a more prominent place in psychiatric thinking.

In addition to postulating causal relationships, we must also assume that our sensory perceptions supported by instruments have some kind of correspondence to events in nature and that our processes of reasoning can in some degree represent actual relationships between these events. We further assume that by repeated multiple and ever more refined observations of nature, and by constant reworking of the logical structure of our hypotheses in the light of these observations, we can achieve not only a widening of knowledge, but also progress through successive approximations toward truth—a greater and greater correspondence between our concepts, and events actually occurring.

You will note that in what has just been said, the processes of reason and the fruits of sense-awareness are both overhung with doubts as to their ability to represent nature. They are both seen as limited means for grasping its characteristics. Of the two, however, I have given greater emphasis to the doubts about the rational processes. There is a purpose in this that has particular bearing on the present status of research in the behavioral sciences, including, of course, social psychiatry, and I should like to take a few moments to explain it.

Objectivity, hypothesis testing, statistical treatment, are aspects of the scientific procedure which at present enjoy high praise. Indeed the words themselves are like price tags which by their very attachment to something can raise its prestige even when they do not very adequately represent its worth. Perhaps a better comparison would be the attachment of famous names to paintings of indifferent merit. In the early nineteenth century when frontier America was awakening to European culture, the land was flooded with paintings that bore names like Rubens, Van Dyke, Reynolds and others. Apparently these, rather than the contents of the pictures, sold them sometimes at a very high price.

I make this comparison, not to imply forgery, but rather to indicate the power of prestigeful words once they gain currency, and to underline their ability to dazzle the eye of critical evaluation. Nor am I attempting to belittle the worth of measurement, statistics, or hypothesis testing, any more than I would belittle Van Dyke by pointing out that a lot of shoddy pictures once circulated with his name on them.

The fact is that mankind has long been puzzled by the unreliability and deceptiveness of the senses. At various times and in various ways, those pushing forward the development of knowledge, have sought refuge from this. Sometimes the turn has been to a limited set of religious articles of faith with a logical super-structure of theology erected on them. At other times, the turn has been to secular assumptions about the nature of reality with certain propositions as foundations upon which all else is built according to strict canons of reason, after the pattern of Euclid. Faith at times has been very high in this approach. There are occasions today when one cannot help being astounded at the blind confidence of some practical men in their notions of reality, particularly with reference to human motivation and the functioning of society.

On the other hand, there are swings away from dependence on rational systems as it is realized that the propositional underpinnings have a habit of sinking into the sand, and that the chains of logic turn out to have breaks in them. The Pythagoreans for instance tried to explain everything in terms of numbers, but came up against the irrationals, and Zeno introduced challenges with his paradoxes. The axioms and self-evident truths of Euclid do not all stand up under close scrutiny and one has to admit the probability that the results of the theorems were actually known first, with the logical structure and axioms derived backward from them.[18]

At the present time we attach great importance to objectivity. As part of the equipment for approaching truth, its value must be unquestioned; but one sometimes hears objectivity spoken about as if it were truth itself. Objectivity means no more than reliability, that observers with a certain specified degree of independence report essentially the same thing. It does not obviate their being nevertheless wrong due to factors it is not possible to take into account in planning the operation. Criteria can be standardized, for instance, in such a way as to consti- tute a standardization of error, a situation which can well arise in connection with such "objective" operations as the reading of X-ray plates and the employment of psy- chological tests. The reports over many years to the effect that there are forty-eight human chromosomes were ex- ceedingly reliable but were, it now appears, not valid. The accepted number today is forty-six.[19]

Even the double and triple blind test may, if the tech- nique is not virtually perfect, be only a way of doubly and triply misleading yourself. Objectivity, hypothesis testing and statistical methods are, of course, procedures that have been long demonstrated as major factors in the advance of knowledge. They are not, however, the whole story. They can be misapplied, prematurely applied and exclusively applied without regard to other dimensions of science. In particular they can be applied at the expense of comprehensive observation, of accurate description of multiple facets, of description of sequences through time, and of comparative analysis, particularly the comparative analysis of complex patterns treated as wholes. These somewhat contrasting procedures are scientific methods which perforce lean heavily on sensory perceptions and often on extensive complex observations, rather than on precise measurement of a limited number of variables. This kind of thing is evident in the practice of clinical medicine and in the various manifestations of natural history such as botany, geology, zoology, anatomy and physiology—in short most of the sciences that deal with living things.

In making this point, I am not maintaining that reliable measurement, hypothesis testing, and statistics are absent from these fields. On the contrary, they are utilized extensively, but they are used and have been used in conjunction with the activities that characterize natural history. In particular I would stress observation, classification, hypothesis seeking and descriptions, both of cross-sections of events, taken at a moment like a section of tissue for the microscope, and of on-going processes of nature through time, like the life cycle of bats or the growth of a child. Determining adequate units for counting is a prerequisite of mensuration.

To sum up, I am suggesting that the behavioral sciences may suffer from an unwillingness to make working assumptions about the validity of sense-awareness, from hesitancy to deal in somewhat broad and at first crude levels of approximation, and equally from too great a confidence in the ability of the rational processes to represent nature even when buttressed with objective measurements and hypotheses that are checked under controlled conditions, and which are subjectable to tests of statistical significance.

There are many exceptions, of course, to the above criticism. In particular, one can point to clinical psychiatry, especially psychoanalysis, as a field where observation and hypothesis building have had full play. Here, I would feel we have gone to the other extreme, and have built theory on theory, and conflict of theory on conflict of theory. The results sometimes appear more like struggles between schoolmen in the Middle Ages than like effort to reduce these ideas to forms that can be put to some kind of test.

It is probable that there has always been vacillation in the pursuit of knowledge between mistrust of observation and mistrust of deductive approaches. The fashion currently is to lean heavily on the latter. The essence of the matter is that neither is wholly trustworthy, but yet we must have both and neither to the exclusion of the other.

I believe that at present there is a tendency to follow too closely the methods of laboratories for physics and chemistry. That the behavioral sciences should try to imitate the methods of the physical sciences is, of course, easy to understand. The success of the latter and their world prestige is a strong admonition for us to go and do likewise. It is, however, more to the point for us to strive to be as good as, rather than the same as, other sciences.

In the words of the Japanese poet Basho, we should not try to follow in the footsteps of the great masters, but "rather seek what they sought."

The current attempt to follow the laboratory sciences has a touch of irony about it. In the nineteenth century there was some disposition for the behavioral sciences as they existed then to imitate the methods of natural history. This was under the influence of the success and renown achieved by Darwin's concepts of organic evolution and natural selection. With Tylor, anthropology was started in an attempt to put the races of man on an evolutionary tree, and Spencer gave sociology a bent toward seeing societies as organisms. In psychology and psychiatry, to a large extent under the influence of Helmholtz, there was the urge to work out all human behavior according to physiological principles. Then there was a coming of age and each behavioral field saw itself as a science in its own right. There was a revulsion against biologizing, an urge in each science to consider itself as a discipline with its own subject matter, its own methods and body of theory. There should be no slavish imitation of biology. This trend was of course worthy. The irony is that in looking over their shoulders as they fled from the dominance of biology, the behavioral sciences ran right into the grip of the physical sciences. One branch of psychology, for instance, attempted to find in sensations the equivalent of the periodic table. Today the model is more apt to be physics. The upshot is that we are now likely to employ orientation and methods which are farther away from rather than closer to those relevant for our subject matter.[20]

The conclusion which I draw from all this is not that

one should return to biologizing human behavior, but to a greater emphasis on the independence of the behavioral sciences and the derivation of their methods from the character of their problems. There should, however, be some looking to other fields for such leads as they can provide, and here I feel that the sciences which also deal in living things have more to offer at the present stage of our development than do those which deal with the inanimate world. The biological sciences have long had to cope with the difficulties of process description, of pattern analysis, of working where the opportunity for laboratory control is excessively limited, and where the effects of experimental interference, the artifact of the instrument itself, is apt to be exceedingly marked. Of particular relevance are the experience and methods developed for selecting key points at which to apply quantification. In physiology, for example, one deals with a morass of interdependent processes which set at least two major limits on mensuration. One, just noted, is the destruction of significant relationships by the act of measurement, while the other is the practical impossibility of measuring all the electrical, thermal, oxidative and other relevant processes, because of their sheer number in the almost infinite varieties of living things. The prerequisite to quantification and statistical analysis is the selection of units more—rather than less—worth counting. Thus, a major aspect of quantification is a grand strategy of setting aside items of secondary importance and choosing the most significant and workable points for attack. Without attention to this matter, neither accuracy nor statistical sophistication can have a valuable yield. The mills they control grind well, but they cannot improve on the grain that is fed to them.

We start then in approaching research in social psychiatry with these several working assumptions: that events have causes, and that sense awareness, measurement with instruments, and the process of reason, including hypothesis testing, can be used with caution in order to move through successive approximations toward understanding these causes.

I would add here one other basic assumption, namely that for any event or class of events we choose to study, cause will be found to have numbers of components, or in other words to be multiple. There will always be a web of interdependent factors and in no case will it be possible to speak correctly of "the cause." There are, however, legitimate questions of relative importance of some causes as compared to others, given the orientation and purpose with which an event is approached.

ETIOLOGY AND
PSYCHIATRIC DISORDER

With the above points by way of background, let us turn to psychiatric disorder as the class of event before us for attention. "What are its causes?" is the central question, and then, in what way can social psychiatry make a contribution—or to put it more accurately, what types of research endeavor for throwing light on this problem can be properly classified as social psychiatry?

As to causes, these can be considered under three broad headings:

1) Heredity
2) Physiological experience
3) Psychological experience

What is meant by the first is sufficiently evident so that it is not necessary to linger over it.

The second, physiological experience, has to do with the effects of virus, bacteria, toxic agents such as lead and alcohol, malnutrition, physical damage to brain or endocrine system and other items of this general sort. These various agents alone or in combination can produce disorders of personality due to well recognized disturbance of the physical systems. It seems probable that many such agents may also be at work in ways and in instances of which we are as yet unaware. In particular it may be that damage can occur *in utero* as in the case

59

of German measles, but with results which are not manifest until much later in the development of the individual.
When they come, the effects may be in the form of some
difficulty in personality development or organization and,
in such a case, may be attributed to heredity or to psychological experience. What I am saying, essentially in parenthesis as we go by this topic, is that here is a matter, the
importance of which may be much greater than is generally recognized.[21]

In speaking of "psychological experience" the reference
is to the well known types of traumatic event of infancy
and childhood which can set the personality off on a
malfunctional sequence of developmental progression.
This is the area of psychoanalytic contribution to our
knowledge and insight about personality formation and
the factors concerned in the evolution of disordered personalities. I would add, however, other psychological experiences occuring later in childhood and in adulthood.
These later events may be regarded, if one prefers, as
precipitating rather than originating the difficulties, but
this should not lead to minimizing their importance, both
as a practical matter and as a matter of theory. "Originating" and "precipitating" are only ways of designating
different aspects of a causal complex, and the question
of their respective importance is again one of viewpoint
and purpose.

It is of course possible to divide each of these main
headings—heredity, physiological experience and psychological experience—into many, many components, each
an appropriate target of emphasis. Taken together, they
provide a basis for making the observation that some
part of each of the areas designated by these headings

are affected by sociocultural processes. For example the cultural patterns of a society can impose certain regularities on mate selection which can have a differential effect on the distribution of hereditary factors bearing on mental health in that society. Similarly sociocultural patterns have a differential effect on the experiences of pregnant women and of children with regard to physiologically noxious agents.

Psychological experience is the aspect of the causal complex that has had the greatest amount of attention in clinical psychiatry, particularly with reference to the influence of sociocultural factors. This emphasis will also be continued in what I have to say in the rest of these pages. Before embarking upon it, however, I wish to note that social psychiatry has a place in making a contribution to the other two main types of causes, heredity and physiological experience.

From what has been said, it can be seen, as suggested earlier, that basic research in social psychiatry which is focussed on etiology does not require an enlargement of the "syndrome" outlined in connection with actions and uses. It implies, rather, an expansion of what was before mentioned as concern with sociocultural processes and their influence on the origin, course and outcome of psychiatric disorder.

There is, however, a converse: the influence of psychiatric disorder on the functioning of sociocultural systems. While there are a few writings here and there that bear on this topic, it has not yet had systematic development. About all one can say is that the effects of sociopathic behavior is discussed from time to time and there are occasional articles and books which touch on the possible consequences for society of psychiatric disorder in persons of historical importance such as George the Third, Nietzsche, and Dostoevski.[22]

SOCIOCULTURAL PROCESS AND PSYCHOLOGICAL EXPERIENCE

In speaking of the sociocultural process, or of socio-cultural environment, reference is made to a number of different kinds of phenomena. It is hard to describe these sharply for the terms available have overlaps as well as a certain amount of variation in their meaning according to who is using them. We may, however, visualize every human being as living in a society and that this society has the unity of an interacting system. For the purposes here it does not much matter whether you put the boundary at a community, national, sub-national or international level. This interacting system can be further considered as composed of a network of roles and as being linked by channels of communication. Pervading the whole are shared opinions, beliefs, and attitudes which may be spoken of as "systems of sentiment." All of these features are, of course, not static, but in motion through time and subject to change.

Now, in whatever way you set the margins of societies, short of taking the whole world as a society, you will find that they differ from each other with regard to the character of their systems, that is with regard to looseness or tightness of interdependent components, and with regard to types of roles, types of communications, and types of sentiments. Moreover, it will be possible to subdivide most large societies so that one can say these same items are very different in their quality and combinations in these subdivisions. Cultural patterns, in short, differ.

The suggestion is, obviously, that these differences in sociocultural systems can make a difference in the appearance, course, and outcome of psychiatric disorders. When mention is made of sociocultural factors that have etiological significance the point of concern is the individual, and the factors are the impinging edge of sociocultural processes which are part of these larger systems. They are the contact points between the person and his society and culture, and as they vary in society, they can give different individuals different kinds of psychological experience. If some psychological experiences are noxious while others are benign, then it is plausible to suppose that different sociocultural groups will have a difference with regard to the relative preponderance of benign and noxious sociocultural factors. Noxious experience, in short, is a function of the sociocultural context. This assumption opens the way, consequently, for an approach to etiology through comparative analysis.

Following on this general proposition, there are a number of additional points for note, and the first of these is the question of when in the life cycle of the individual, sociocultural factors can have an impact. A second and closely related question is how such an impact is conceived to be transmuted into what, from a psychiatric point of view, could be regarded as an important psychological experience.

Obviously, infancy and childhood constitute periods of a person's life-arc that are of major significance in this regard. There are some clinicians who would maintain that sociocultural factors can make very little difference, on the ground that while psychiatric disorder is based in a large measure on psychological experience, it is at such an early and primitive level that sociocultural factors can have little influence. This view would seem to lean heavily on assumptions regarding constitutional predisposition, or certain inherent difficulties in the parent-child relationship and symbolic functions common the world over.[23]

An alternative view is that the way the mother treats the child—the timing of nursing, weaning, toilet training and the rest, and particularly the emotional tone that goes with these—makes a difference in personality formation and these differences are fraught with significance for mental health. Beyond the mother-child relationship, there is the relationship with the father, with the siblings, and the interactions of all of those constituting a family system, which as a whole has an effect on the individual we are considering. It is not difficult to perceive that different social systems and different sub-systems must have a consistent influence on such family patterns. Culture and sub-culture in short make a difference regarding the psychological experience of the infant and young child, a difference which can be large or small depending on the particular groups being brought into comparison.

Even though, however, infancy and childhood are times of great importance in these matters, it is not necessary to consider them the whole story. Later periods of childhood can also be regarded as times when the formation of personality is still going on, and hence as subject to malformation from psychological experience. Adolescence may be a period of particular susceptibility, and here too sociocultural factors can be supposed as making a difference.

In looking at the adult part of life, some advantage may be gained from considering the situation in terms of stress. Thus, certain sociocultural situations, as compared to others, may apply stress to the individual such as to push him in the direction of reacting with one or another of the patterns called psychiatric disorder.

Finally, once psychiatric disorder has developed, the characteristics of the sociocultural environment may offer helps and opportunities for recovery, or they may confirm one in the disordered pattern of reaction. This difference is not dependent on the presence or absence of formal psychiatric services, but also on other resources that can offer aid such as wise listeners among clergy, general practitioners, and other even less formal gatekeepers of the society, and on the quality of some associations as in those pertaining to church, recreation, and fraternal organizations that can have a therapeutic effect.

To over-simplify, then, the impinging edge of the sociocultural process can be conceived as affecting personality for better or worse in three ways, as the individual passes through his life arc: 1) As formative influences during personality development; 2) as stress laid on adult personality; and 3) as patterns disposing toward recovery or confirmation in disorder, once the latter has developed.

Research regarding the role of psychological experience in the development of psychiatric disorder is approachable through a number of disciplines. It is obvious that there is a large field here for clinical studies, and the employment of the techniques of both psychiatry and psychology. Social psychiatry is but one contributor, one that deals in those aspects of etiology in which social and cultural factors play, or are seen as probably playing, a major part in determining and modifying the psychological experiences. The fact that these in turn pertain to the inner working of personality means that social psychiatry has a linking part to play between cultural studies and psychodynamic studies.[24]

SOME AREAS FOR RESEARCH

Having narrowed our point of attention thus far, and to some extent set it in its context, a few illustrative problems for research in etiology through social psychiatry may now be mentioned.

One way of going at the matter is through defining noxious situations. As a result of clinical experience and the theories of dynamic psychiatry derived therefrom, it is possible to postulate certain recurrent situations or constellations of sociocultural factors as having a high probability of inducing, or at least fostering, the emergence of psychiatric disorder among those on whom they impinge. Such potentially noxious patterns can then be studied in a variety of different attending circumstances in order to determine under what conditions they lead to psychiatric disorder and under what conditions they lead to some other pattern.

To illustrate, the loss of a mother during infancy or early childhood is an event that occurs more often in some societies than others and in some parts of our own society as compared to other parts. There is, however, great variation in attending circumstances. For example the loss may be poorly compensated and accompanied by other deprivations of love and of physical needs, or it may be accompanied by prompt replacement with another mothering one, as might occur among the Navahos, with

68

no additional discomfort. All sorts of combinations of factors are possible, and systematic, comparative studies which take advantage of nature's experiments can look forward to unwrapping gradually the central factors so far as psychiatric disorder is concerned.

Maternal deprivation is but one instance. There are many other recurrent pot holes in the various sociocultural systems which can be selected on the basis of clinical conceptions and investigated through comparative and longitudinal studies.

Another problem area may be called "intensive personality studies." By this is meant the investigation of nonpatients, as well as patients. The aim would be to achieve a comparative analysis of ill and presumably well people in order to discover significant differences in terms of experience with sociocultural factors. It is not likely, however, that significance could be established through the intensive personality studies alone. Extensive studies would also be necessary in order to make generalizations with regard to incidence and hence with regard to the reality of the presumed causal relationships. The intensive studies would show how multiple complex factors interact across a time span in selected cases and by this means set up targets for determination by extensive techniques. Out of all this, one could hope to draw some understanding of how and why a given sociocultural environment affects some persons adversely, and how and why the interaction of others with the environment results in patterns of adaptation that are functionally adequate or even superior. Such comparative investigations conducted at least in part with people as they are living in their communities, could lead in time to more adequate definitions of both mental health and psychiatric disorder.

The comparative study of cultures also presents an opportunity for investigation. This encompasses a very broad range of possibilities with many technical difficulties. The inherent logic of the proposal is, however, clear enough: if different sociocultural systems have different effects with regard to personality formation, to the stresses laid on adult personality, and to facility for the development and maintenance of symptoms, then comparative observations, comparative analyses and even comparative experiments aimed at treatment and prevention should be revealing important causal factors in psychiatric disorder.

A still different approach may be advanced under the heading of prevalence and incidence studies. Here we start with psychiatric disorders themselves and attempt to plot their distribution in the sociocultural system. The aim is to know every instance of psychiatric disorder in a given population and to see these projected against the sociocultural features. By this means, associations between main features of the sociocultural environment and one or more types of psychiatric disorder may be discerned. Such associations can then become the objective of more refined or crucial research designed to ascertain whether this association is due to a casual relationship between environment and disorder. Discovering the distribution of psychiatric disorder in the sociocultural environment can provide information of major importance in reaching a more exact understanding of etiology. It can remove from the realm of speculation much that is necessarily speculative so long as research is done in the clinical framework alone. A firm understanding of cause will require some eventual synthesis of these two lines of investigation together with studies of heredity and of physiological experiences. The point about prevalence and incidence studies is that they hold an essential piece of the jigsaw puzzle which constitutes etiology, and in this rests their importance for clinical psychiatry.

I have described prevalence and incidence studies as if they were entirely a fishing expedition to ascertain association between environmental features and psychiatric disorders. They need not, however, be quite so wide open; they can be combined with the study of noxious situations. Through studying the nature of the socio-cultural environment and by laying this against clinical knowledge, it is possible to predict that certain associations will be found. This amounts to making hypotheses and then gathering data to see whether or not they tend to support the hypotheses. Thus, hypothesis seeking can be combined with hypothesis checking.

In order to give these remarks substance let me report to you a few figures based on the study of a rural county. These are estimates of the true prevalence of psychiatric disorders. I say they are "estimates" because they are based on a sample, not a total count, and on symptoms employed as indicators rather than on diagnoses. "True" is used because the point at issue is the distribution of disorder in the population regardless of whether or not there has been diagnosis and treatment. "Prevalence" means the number of people estimated to have psychiatric disorder at a given moment. It is to be distinguished from "incidence," which refers to the number of new cases emerging over a period of time.

In broad terms the prevalence of symptoms is as follows for adults who are also heads of households in a county with a total population of 20,000. The sample itself contained a little over 1,000, which is about 1/5 of the household heads.

Brain Syndrome	3%
Mental Deficiency	5%
Affective psychoses	0.3%
Schizophrenic psychoses	0.5%
Psychophysiological disorders	59%
Psychoneuroses	52%
Personality disorders	6%
Sociopathic disorders	6%

The labels employed in this listing require some explanation. They are based on the terms and definitions suggested in the American Psychiatric Association's *Diagnostic and Statistical Manual, Mental Disorders,* published in 1952. The usage here, however, differs in that the words do not stand for diagnoses but rather symptom clusters, constituting eight more or less different types. Specifically, there are no dynamic or etiological implications. "Brain Syndrome" therefore, refers to people with a pattern of symptoms *characteristic* of some kind of organic brain disorder, but it does not mean that the organic factors have been investigated and identified. Nearly all of the people placed in this category were, in fact, showing the symptom clusters characteristic of senility and arteriosclerosis—intermittent disorientation, confusion, or loss of recent memory.

"Mental Deficiency" refers to any degree of retardation

that could be detected through our kind of interview and by information from collateral sources but without psychological tests. It is a relatively crude device and our guess is that most of the people categorized thus had an I.Q. below 80. But again, the reference is only to symptoms charactertistic of retardation, and does not rule out the possibility that some of the people so listed may have had emotional or schizophrenic factors as accountable for their behavior.

"Affective psychoses" means severe depressive symptoms while "schizophrenic" refers to evidence of "typical thinking disorder."

"Psychophysiological" stands for symptoms of organic quality which we suppose are commonly rooted in emotional difficulties. Characteristic of this group are gastrointestinal disturbances, cardio-vascular symptoms, hay fever and asthma.

"Psychoneurotic" symptoms encompass for the most part manifestations of anxiety, while "personality" disorders are more diffuse, such as life-long emotional instability.

"Sociopathic" covers many forms of anti- and dissocial behavior, but in the study of this county it turns out to be mainly alcoholism.

Since our findings are based on a sample of people living in the county and currently functioning as heads of households, all cases that have been hospitalized are, obviously, omitted.

Turning now to the figures, it may be noted that the percentages add up to more than 100. This is because one individual frequently has more than one type of symptom pattern. Conversely there are those who have no symptoms at all, according to the methods used.

Some additional qualifying considerations are as follows. Among those who do have symptoms, many are not greatly discomfitted or impaired by them, nor do they present marked problems to other persons. Impairment is, therefore, an important matter for estimating significant morbidity. It is also a difficult one, due to questions of establishing consistent and reliable criteria. There are, too, problems of choosing among alternative cutting points between the impaired and the unimpaired and this in turn depends on purpose. Finally, understanding of the results requires a fairly accurate understanding of the methods employed. The providing of this information demands a volume in itself and such is being prepared.[25] Pending its appearance, there seems no choice but to offer here the summary conclusions of those who have been active in the study. Using ability to work as the main reference point for impairment we believe that among household heads in this county the following obtains:

No symptom patterns   19%

Symptom patterns but no significant

impairment 50%

Symptom patterns and significant impairment 31%

The 31 per cent who are impaired to a significant degree, are not for the most part disabled. The vast majority of them are in a "mild" category, but all are estimated as having at least 10 per cent of their life-space consumed by their symptoms. I should also add that this is in our opinion a minimal figure. More intensive investigation would probably send it higher.

Beyond the question of sheer numbers, is the problem

of how the people with various kinds of impairing symptoms are distributed in the sociocultural systems. It is through the investigation of this matter that we begin to move in the direction of etiological understanding. One example may serve to illustrate the approach, and can be presented in terms of an hypothesis that has been submitted to some measure of checking with evidence.

Briefly the hypothesis is that a disintegrated sociocultural environment will produce disintegrated personalities. What I mean by sociocultural disintegration is a rather complicated matter, but let me give the flavor of it by saying that a disintegrated group exhibits a relative lack of leadership, of followership, of stable social institutions, of systematic interpersonal relationships and of reasonably clear sentiments. It is, as a sociocultural system, sprawling, malfunctional, lethargic and unpredictable. Clearly, as a sociocultural environment it would tend toward the malformation of personalities growing up there, would place severe psychological stress on the adults, and would offer few or no forms of indigenous therapy, but rather confirm people in their psychiatric disorders.[26]

Neighborhoods and communities were identified as disintegrated and well integrated in the county we studied through the use of anthropological and sociological techniques. This was carried out with as much independence as possible from the operation whereby the prevalence of people with symptoms was estimated. As already noted, sampling techniques were employed to select respondents and in addition to this, the psychiatric evaluation of symptom patterns was done in such a way as to prevent the evaluators from knowing the part of the county from which any given respondent came. This was possible because the psychiatrists doing the evaluations worked from transcripts of the interviews conducted by a trained staff.

Analysis of results indicate that there were about twice as many individuals with impairing symptoms in the disintegrated group as in the others. Moreover, the people had a greater number of symptoms per head, and appeared generally sicker.

This finding can be used to point up some of the remarks made earlier about the character of this kind of research. Although the evidence bears on the hypothesis it does not prove it. It could be, for instance, that instead of a disintegrated society generating psychiatric disorder, it is rather the other way around. Disordered personalities might get precipitated together by the processes of the larger society and thus form, because of their characteristics, disintegrated groups. The causal emphasis may thus not lie in the sociocultural environment, but in heredity. There is some evidence against this in the history of these particular disintegrated groups, but it remains a possible alternative explanation pointing the way for more work. It presents a difficult question in the way of further progress, but not, I think, an insoluble one.

Another point to recognize is our inadequate knowledge regarding the importance of physiological experience—such factors as malnutrition, subclinical disease, and injuries sustained before, during and after birth, particularly injuries that are for a time quiescent, only showing their effects much later in the development of the individual. Disintegrated communities may well be high in noxious events of this type and so exert an effect on the prevalence of psychiatric disorder more through physiological experience than through psychological.

A still different point to note is that even if the main etiological factors are psychological, our study tells us little as to how these actually work. The links are still missing between the sociocultural factors and the dynamics of personality. A whole sheaf of different explanations of the relationships seen could be laid out. In order to choose the most probable among them for additional investigation, intensive personality studies of the type noted earlier would have to be devised.

There are other questions raised by the prevalence survey, quite apart from the problems of this integration-disintegration hypothesis. When our figures are mentioned, people are apt to be stirred by the size of the percentages quoted with regard to the prevalence of symptoms and their implication regarding the prevalence of disorder. Thirty-one per cent is a large part of a population, even if for most of the individuals the impairment is not severe. Our readers and hearers have some tendency to be incredulous and to look for other explanations.

One of these is that the county selected was unusual, that it contains much more in the way of psychiatric disorder than one would find in most places. This remains to be determined by the eventual reduplication of such studies in other regions. What one can say at present is that there are no reasons for thinking the county is unusual in this regard. Indeed one may wonder if the figures are so surprising, given the vast sales of tranquilizers in North America and elsewhere. The Midtown

Study conducted in Manhattan by the late Thomas A. C. Rennie is also a point of reference because like the Stirling County Study the aim was to estimate true prevalence. While there are marked differences of method and sampling between the two investigations, it is noteworthy that the general order of prevalence of findings is similar.[27]

Another possible explanation is that the instrument we used for making our estimates was at fault. It could be that psychiatrists are prone to magnify the indicators of pathology and it may not be wise to take these figures at their face-value.

There may be something in this interpretation, but if it is true, it is a matter of profound significance for clinical psychiatry. It implies a major overhaul of many of the criteria both implicit and explicit in terms of which we make diagnosis and evaluate the progress of our patients on the road to recovery. It points to the need for re-examining these criteria through systematic comparisons of samples of patients and samples of non-patients, and for laying down some observational and even experimental bases for a concept of mental health.

It could be, of course, that the matter is not so complicated but rather rests with peculiarities in the particular psychiatrists who did the study. While admitting to the possibility of a prejudiced view I must say I think this unlikely, for considerable pains were taken to secure multiple independent judges and to compare them with each other. Altogether, eight different psychiatrists and one general practitioner were involved in making the evaluations of the Stirling and Midtown Studies, or in checking methods and criteria. Between them they represented a wide range in type of training and background.

I suspect that the concept of health or wellness is a weak-point. Given that an individual is in trouble and presumably a psychiatric case—which is the context in which we see most of our patients—we can probably discern signs and symptoms and interpret them in a manner that has validity and which represents some, at least, of the inner workings and malfunctionings of persons. On the other hand, given similar signs and symptoms in an individual who is to all intents and purposes functioning adequately we may not know quite what to do with them. We lack systematic knowledge regarding the dynamics of well people; we even lack an adequate and generally accepted basis for recognizing wellness. The closest approach to this we have is the pragmatic criterion of absence of those patterns of behavior which we customarily regard as symptoms. This is not satisfactory, but the road out of this situation is research rather than making assertions about the nature of mental health.

It remains possible that these prevalence estimates *are to be* taken at their face value, or close to it. At the risk of seeming to contradict myself, I should like to say that I have reasonable confidence that this, too, is the case. I think that while it is true that we psychiatrists have a somewhat intemperate tendency to see pathology in the human beings we consider, and that there is reason to call some of our criteria in question, at the same time I do not think this is sufficient to account altogether for the magnitude of the prevalence figures. For, when in the present study, we have examined sub-samples more closely and with the benefit of more information, the percentage of people with impairing symptoms has increased, not decreased. It should be borne in mind again that most of these impairments are mild rather than moderate or severe. Nevertheless, they present a picture of something like a third of the adult population having symptoms characteristic of psychiatric patients and suffering a measure of unhappiness and difficulty in their work because of them.

If this is true, it impels one toward certain conclusions with regard to clinical psychiatry and raises some insistent questions. Since these conclusions and questions imply modifications in existing goals, sentiments and customs, they are not apt to be popular, and there may consequently be some tendency to avoid the whole business, or to attack and then dismiss epidemiological efforts in psychiatry.

One conclusion is that if something around a third of the population are comparable to the people seen in clinics and in private practice, then the present form of psychiatric services is never going to be adequate for coping with the need. Such would be impossible on at least two counts. One is the matter of personnel—there are not now and are never likely to be enough psychiatrists. The other is the economic factor; the cost of treatment on such a scale is something which could not be borne on either a public or a private basis.

There is, furthermore, the possibility that treatment by means of psychotherapy or drugs is not the best answer for numbers of these people. If environmental factors are important in the precipitation and maintenance of disorder, then it may be impossible for many of the people to recover until their circumstances are changed.

Looking at the matter from the point of view of our

civilization's value sentiments, one can question the rightness of trying to change people rather than their condition under certain circumstances. Are not some forms of adjustment undesirable? Should people adjust to prevailing instabilities in their society, to oppression, to cruelty, and to dishonesty, to frightening unreliability of mass media of communication? to fruitless systems of competition that prevent development of resources and capacities in personality? Are not some forms of adjustment to some kinds of environment to be regarded as pathological, so costly to personality, as to resemble the fish which adjust to life in caves by losing their eyes?

Prevention is one recourse. Again the question of "How?" comes up, but this time the accent in the reply is on research. Although I said earlier that we know more than we practice, I would add now that we do not know enough. There is need for applied research in order to advance further toward goals already clear. Even greater, however, is the need to push research with regard to how prevention can be done.

Perhaps it is impossible. Perhaps the task is imbedded in the larger problems of the total character of our civilization's state of accelerated change, and rhythms of world-wide violence. On the other hand, perhaps there can be discoveries, if the problem is tackled in sufficient force and with sufficient discrimination. Perhaps if ways can be found to reduce the total load of psychiatric disorder, psychiatry can make a contribution toward solving some of the root problems of the conglomerate of sociocultural systems which cover the world.

This need for prevention, raises questions as to the way psychiatric man-power is presently deployed. The vast preponderance is in therapy, and only a very small trickle is concerned with matters that will ever have a significant impact on the prevalence of disorder. This is a very grave consideration.

The apparent distribution of true prevalence in society brings a related set of questions. Numbers of studies show that by far the greatest amount of psychiatric disorder is in those very segments of society which have the least service. This is true of the disintegrated communities I mentioned earlier, and it is true of people at the lower socioeconomic levels in cities where these have been studied. It is not just a matter of the services being unavailable and more directed at people in the middle and upper levels. Clinics, including those which provide psychotherapy, do exist. The problem is much more profound. It lies in the apparent difficulty the psychiatrist has in understanding and communicating with such people, and equally in their difficulty in understanding the meaning of their complaints and in grasping the concepts of psychiatry. The upshot is that here is a large population, in fact the largest population of people with psychiatric disorders, and yet they are almost untouched and unknown to psychiatry, except when they become psychotic and receive organic and custodial types of care.[28]

CONCLUSION

To review briefly, it will be recalled that Part I of this book was concerned with the actions and uses of social psychiatry. These were seen in such contexts as the courts, industry, community and in psychiatric institutions viewed as sociocultural systems. Social psychiatry was distinguished from clinical psychiatry by its emphasis on people in numbers, on the interaction of sociocultural and psychological processes, on responsibility to a group, on conducting psychiatric knowledge to strategic points in the sociocultural system so as to foster a reduction in psychiatric disorder and to promote greater human happiness, and on conducting relevant knowledge from the social sciences into clinical psychiatry. It was further suggested that as a practical matter, a number of opportunities exist for still wider and more intensive use of social psychiatry. In many of the activities mentioned it was maintained that less is practiced than is known, and that there is room for expansion.

Beyond this, some essentially new fields were seen as awaiting development. One of these is the creation of preventive teams somewhat after the models found in public health. Such teams, composed not only of psychiatrists, but of other behavioral scientists as well, could take as their focus communities, or subdivisions of communities such as industrial plants, and schools. These human groups would be assessed for the presence of patterns tending to foster psychiatric disorder, the noxious spots in the systems brought to light, and remedial measures worked out with the people of the groups concerned.

A second kind of team is one for tackling the problems of humanizing the changes occurring in underdeveloped areas—which is to say most of the world. Finally it was suggested that attention be given to change in our own society in which the acceleration of the industrial revolution is now being compounded by automation and nuclear energy. Overhanging all of this are the unprecedented problems of masses of people living for years and years under a constant threat of annihilation while all kinds of psychological warfare is flashed in rotation.

In these grave matters, psychiatry is of course only one of numbers of potential contributors from the behavioral sciences. It may be considered as having three main sources from which to draw: knowledge of psychopathology; knowledge of human motivation; and experience in dealing with human personality conceived as a whole, as a self-integrating unit.

Part II has been concerned with the research aspect of social psychiatry, the widening of knowledge. In its most practical phase this is primarily a service for the better application of social psychiatry along one or more of the lines already evident. Continuous with applied research, however, is an extended field of basic research within the general orientation of an emphasis on people in numbers, and the interplay of sociocultural and psychological processes. Some underlying assumptions with regard to the nature of basic research were pointed out and suggestions made concerning the need for adapting concepts and methods to the character of the problems, rather than an uncritical borrowing from other sciences.

The etiology of psychiatric disorders with reference to the role of sociocultural factors was given a central position as a topic of concern in basic research, and an attempt was made to set this in some perspective in relation to hereditary and physiological factors. Note was also taken of the probability that sociocultural factors, mediated through psychological experience, have differential effects on personality at different phases of the life-arc from infancy onward. Etiology was considered somewhat broadly in terms of not only the origin, but also the course and outcome of psychiatric disorders.

A number of problems and problem areas were sketched in order to provide some illustrative examples of research in social psychiatry directed at questions of etiology. Among those, studies of prevalence were held up for particular attention since they occupy a position of central importance, given the present level of our knowledge. Associations between frequency of disorder and sociocultural factors or processes have to be established as a preliminary to further investigation for possible causal relationships. A sample of findings from one study was presented in order to make some of the concepts, methods and problems in question a little more tangible.

In looking over the spread of social psychiatry, both as action and as research, it seems evident that it constitutes an opportunity and a challenge. The opportunity is in the application of evident knowledge to evident problems by means of evident techniques. It also lies in the possibility of discovery, through research, of more efficient approaches to these same problems.

The challenge lies in the fact that we do not practice as much as we know, and do not know as much as we could. The importance of this is self-evident in the air of the times in which we live, where emotionally upset people are confronted with ever more difficult problems. Mounting evidence points to a prevalence of human suffering and human wastage that present forms of therapy can never meet. While there must always be treatment and the helping of the maladjusted personality to adjust, there is also need to adjust the sociocultural system. Psychiatry is faced with playing a part in the changing of society and the changing of culture.

These are formidable questions for our discipline, for those now undergoing training and planning their lives as psychiatrists, and for institutions engaged in teaching and training.

NOTES

NOTES

1. A selected bibliography is provided below for these eight examples of social psychiatry. The items have been chosen with a view to supplying a few main references and so helping an interested reader begin exploring these fields.

a. **Psychiatry and the Law**

Brancale, Ralph: Diagnostic techniques in aid of sentencing, *Law and Contemporary Problems, Vol. 23*: p. 442, 1958.

Davidson, Henry A.: *Forensic Psychiatry*, New York, Ronald Press, 1952.

Guttmacher, M. S. and Weihofen, H.: *Psychiatry and the Law*, New York, W. W. Norton, 1952.

Hoch, Paul H. and Zubin, Joseph (eds.): *Psychiatry and the Law*, London, New York, Grune and Stratton, 1955.

Overholser, W.: *The Psychiatrist and the Law*, New York, Harcourt Brace, 1953.

b. **Military Psychiatry**

Ahrenfeldt, Robert H.: *Psychiatry in the British Army in the Second World War*, New York, Columbia University Press, 1958.

Ginzberg, Eli: *The Ineffective Soldier*, three volumes, New York, Columbia University Press, 1959.

Ginzberg, Eli, Herma, John L., and Ginsburg, Sol W.:

Psychiatry and Military Manpower Policy, New York, King's Crown Press, Columbia University, 1953.

Mandelbaum, David G.: Psychiatry in military society, *Human Organization, Vol. 13:* No. 3, 1954, and *Vol. 13:* No. 4, 1955.

Menninger, W. C.: *Psychiatry in a Troubled World,* New York, The Macmillan Co., 1948.

c. **Educational Psychiatry**

Darling, Douglas C.: The multidisciplinary approach to the solution of student mental health problems, *Mental Hygiene, Vol. 41:* No. 2, April 1957, pp. 170-177.

Farnsworth, Dana L.: *Mental Health in College and University,* Cambridge, Harvard University Press, 1957.

Wedge, Bryant M. (ed.): *Psychosocial Problems of College Men,* New Haven, Yale University Press, 1958.

Considerations on personality development in college students, *Group for the Advancement of Psychiatry Report, No. 32:* May 1955.

The role of psychiatrists in colleges and universities, *Group for the Advancement of Psychiatry Report, No. 17:* January 1957.

The role of the college in student maturation, *Group for the Advancement of Psychiatry Circular Letter, No. 274:* Dec. 1957.

d. **Industrial Psychiatry**

American Psychiatric Association: Troubled people on the job, *Committee on Occupational Psychiatry,* American Psychiatric Association, Washington, D.C.; 1959.

Burling, Temple: You can't hire a hand, *Extension Bulletin* No. 2, Ithaca, New York; New York State

School of Industrial and Labor Relations, 1952.

Burling, Temple: Essays on human aspects of administration, *Extension Bulletin* No. 25, Ithaca, New York; New York State School of Industrial and Labor Relations, August 1953.

Burling, Temple and Longaker, William D.: Training for industrial psychiatry, *American Journal of Psychiatry, Vol. 3*: No. 7, January 1955.

Jaques, Elliott: *The Changing Culture in a Factory*, London, Tavistock Publications, 1951.

McLean, Alan A. and Taylor, Graham C.: *Mental Health in Industry*, New York, McGraw Hill, 1958.

Mental Health of the Worker, *Public Health Reports, Vol. 74*: No. 8, August 1959.

e. Government Psychiatry

Although a certain amount has been done and is currently going on, literature dealing with one or another aspect of Government Psychiatry is scarce. Some of the items listed below overlap with other fields and include more than psychiatry. The Bunker and Adair book and the volume edited by Spicer are given because they have emanated from a project directed by a psychiatrist.

Bunker, Robert, and Adair, John: *The First Look at Strangers*, New Brunswick, N. J., Rutgers University Press, 1959.

Daugherty, William E. in collaboration with Janowitz, Morris: *A Psychological Warfare Casebook*, Baltimore, Md., The Johns Hopkins Press, 1958.

Duhl, Leonard J., M.D.: City responsibilities in problems of mental health, presented at the *34th Annual Municipal Congress of the American Municipal Association*, San Francisco, December 3, 1957.

Leighton, Alexander H.: *Human Relations in a Changing World,* New York, E. P. Dutton, 1949.

Line, William, and King, Margery R., (eds.): *Mental Health in Public Affairs, A Report of the Fifth International Congress on Mental Health,* Toronto, University of Toronto Press, 1956.

Spicer, Edward H. (ed.): *Human Problems in Technological Change,* New York, Russell Sage Foundation, 1952.

Mental health problems of automation, *World Health Organization, Technical Report Series, No. 183,* Geneva 1959.

The use of psychiatrists in government in relation to international problems, *Group for the Advancement of Psychiatry Report, No. 28:* August 1954.

Report on homosexuality with particular emphasis on this problem in governmental agencies, *Group for the Advancement of Psychiatry Report, No. 30:* January 1955.

Working abroad: a discussion of psychological attitudes and adaptations in new situations, *Group for the Advancement of Psychiatry Report, No. 41:* Dec. 1958.

f. **Psychiatric Institutions considered as social systems**
Caudill, William: *A Psychiatric Hospital as a Small Society,* Cambridge Mass., Harvard University Press, 1958.

Stanton, Alfred H. and Schwartz, Morris S.: *The Mental Hospital,* New York, Basic Books, 1954.

g. **Group Psychotherapy**
Frank, Jerome D.: Some aspects of cohesiveness and conflict in psychiatric out-patient groups, *Bulletin of the Johns Hopkins Hospital, Vol. 101:* No. 4, pp.

224-231, October 1957.

Frank, Jerome D. and Powdermaker, Florence B.: Group psychotherapy, in *American Handbook of Psychiatry*, Silvano Arieti, (ed.) New York, Basic Books, 1959.

Opler, Marvin K.: Group psychotherapy: individual and cultural dynamics in a group process, *American Journal of Psychiatry, Vol. 114*: No. 5, Nov. 1957.

Powdermaker, Florence B. and Frank, Jerome D.: *Group Psychotherapy*, Cambridge, Mass., Harvard University Press, 1953.

Slavson, S. R. (ed.): *The Fields of Group Psychotherapy*, New York, International University Press, 1956.

h. Community Psychiatry

Aberle, David: Introducing preventive psychiatry into a community, *Human Organization, Vol. 9*: No. 3, 1950.

Coleman, M. D. and Zwerling, I.: The psychiatric emergency clinic: a flexible way of meeting community mental health needs, *The American Journal of Psychiatry, Vol. 115*: No. 11, May 1959.

Kotinsky, Ruth and Witmer, Helen L. (eds.): *Community Programs for Mental Health*, Cambridge, Mass., Harvard University Press, 1955.

Leighton, Alexander H. and Longaker, Alice: The psychiatric clinic as a community innovation, *Explorations in Social Psychiatry*, Leighton, A. H., Clausen, John A., and Wilson, Robert N. (eds.), New York, Basic Books, 1957.

Stevenson, George S.: *Mental Health Planning for Social Action*, New York, McGraw Hill, 1956.

The elements of a community mental health program,

Papers presented at the 1955 Annual Conference of the Milbank Memorial Fund, New York, Milbank Memorial Fund, 1955.

2. The McNaghten Rule maintains that in order to establish a defense on the ground of insanity, it must be proved that the accused "was laboring under such a defect of reason, from disease of the mind, as not to know the nature and quality of the act he was doing, or if he did know it, that he did not know what he was doing was wrong." The rule was propounded in England in 1843 and was the result of five questions put to fifteen judges. See Guttmacher, M. S. and Weihofen, H.: *Psychiatry and the Law,* New York, W. W. Norton and Co., 1952, p. 403.

3. The word "sentiment" is employed in these pages in a technical sense based largely on Shand and McDougal. It is not to be confused with sentimental. For an explanation see:

Leighton, Alexander H.: *My Name is Legion,* New York, Basic Books, 1959, pp. 226-275, and 395-420.

4. Saying that the use of societal influences for therapeutic ends is an invention by psychiatry is in all probability true only in a formal sense. While psychiatry has undoubtedly given the topic recognition and promulgated a body of concepts, theories and methods, it seems likely that the principle itself has been discovered many times by all kinds of people and groups throughout history.

The plausibility of this has been brought home to me by observation made in the course of an epidemiological investigation of psychiatric disorders. In the Stirling County Study (see Acknowledgments and also Note

24), an attempt was made to ascertain the prevalence of people with psychiatric symptoms in a small town. In the course of this, two business enterprises attracted attention because of the proportion of persons they contained with a history of fairly serious sociopathic, psychotic, and psychoneurotic disorder. Closer scrutiny revealed that each was headed by a man who in the past had had symptoms to a marked degree, who had brought these under control and then gradually in subsequent years added other persons to his staff who were in difficulties. In each instance, the man or woman added appeared to exhibit a reduction of symptoms. The enterprises were, apparently, therapeutic groups, as well as being successful from a business point of view—one of them outstandingly so. To the best of our knowledge no formal psychiatric help was ever utilized. What was apparently happening is suggestive of Maxwell Jones' "therapeutic community" at Belmont Hospital, near London, and we have come to refer to these two groups in the small town as "Spontaneous Belmonts."

The topic invites further study, both in this town and in other communities in order to discover how frequent an occurrence such activities may be, their effectiveness, the factors that give rise to them and their mode of operation. One would not, furthermore, need to confine his attention to economic enterprises, but could well look over a wide range of associations, including particularly church and recreational groups. Alcoholics Anonymous is probably an instance of something which has many less formal parallels.

See:

Jones, Maxwell: *Social Psychiatry: A Study of Thera-*

peutic Communities, London, Tavistock Publications, 1952.

5. See:

Leighton, Alexander H. and Smith, Robert J.: A comparative study of social and cultural change, *Proceedings of the American Philosophical Society, Vol. 99*: No. 2, April 1955.

6. See for example:

Arensberg, C. (ed.): *Research in Industrial Human Relations*, New York, Harper, 1957.

Landsberger, H.: *Hawthorne Revisited*, Ithaca, New York, Cornell University Press, 1958.

Mayo, Elton: *The Social Problems of an Industrial Civilization*, Cambridge, Mass., Harvard University Press, 1945.

Mayo, Elton, *The Human Problems of an Industrial Civilization*, Cambridge, Mass., Harvard University Press, 1946.

Whyte, William F. (ed.): *Industry and Society*, New York, McGraw-Hill, 1946.

Whyte, William F.: *Man and Organization*, Homewood, Ill., Richard D. Irwin, Inc., 1959.

For an instance of work involving the collaboration of a human relations specialist and psychiatrist see:

Argyris, Chris and Taylor, Graham: The member-centered conference as a research method, in *Human Organization, Vol. 9*: No. 4, 1950 and *Vol. 10*: No. 1, 1951.

7. The first volume of the series from the Joint Commission provides an introduction to the concept of positive mental health. While admiring the book as a whole and the clear way in which Marie Jahoda presents a

difficult topic, my inclinations are more in keeping with those expressed in a largely dissenting chapter at the end by Walter E. Barton.

See: Jahoda, Marie: *Current Concepts of Positive Mental Health*, New York, Basic Books, 1958.

8. For some critical discussions of prevailing legal doctrines and judicial procedures in the light of modern psychiatric information see:

Alexander, F. and Staub, H.: *The Criminal, the Judge and the Public*, (Rev. Ed.), Glencoe, Ill., Free Press, 1956.

*Dession, G. H.: Psychiatry and the conditioning of criminal justice, *Yale Law Journal, Vol. 47*: p. 319, 1938.

Glueck, S.: Principles of a rational penal code, *Harvard Law Review, Vol. 41*: p. 453, 1928.

Guttmacher, M. S.: The psychiatric approach to crime and correction, *Law and Contemporary Problems, Vol. 23*: p. 633, 1958.

*Hall, J.: Psychiatry and criminal responsibility, *Yale Law Journal, Vol. 65*: p. 761, 1956.

*Pilpel, Harriet F.: The job lawyers shirk, *Harper's Magazine Vol. 220*: No. 1316, p. 67, January 1960.

Roche, P. Q.: *The Criminal Mind*, New York, Farrar, Straus and Cudahy, Inc., 1958.

Waelder, R.: Psychiatry and the problem of criminal responsibility, *University of Pennsylvania Law Review, Vol. 101*: p. 378, 1952.

Watson, A. S.: A critique of the legal approach to crime and correction, *Law and Contemporary Problems, Vol. 23*: p. 611, 1958.

*Weihofen, H.: *The Urge to Punish*, New York, Farrar,

Straus and Cudahy, Inc., 1956.

The starred items are by lawyers, and the rest are by psychiatrists. With regard to psychiatry in law schools, the National Institute of Mental Health is sponsoring a number of such programs. See:

Watson, *supra*, p. 629;

also see:

Watson, A. S.: The law and behavioral science project at the University of Pennsylvania: a psychiatrist on the law faculty, *Journal of Legal Education, Vol. 11*, p. 73, 1958.

9. The mutual influence of psychiatry and religion can be seen in such organizations as the National Academy of Religion and Psychiatry and in such publications as:

Some considerations of early attempts in cooperation between religion and psychiatry, *Group for the Advancement of Psychiatry Symposium* No. 5, March 1958.

Psychiatry and religion: some steps toward mutual understanding and usefulness, *Group for the Advancement of Psychiatry Circular Letter, No. 296,* October 1959.

Klausner, Samuel Z. (ed.): *Preliminary Annotated Bibliography and Directory of Workers in the Field of Religion and Psychiatry,* (Mimeographed, 250 pages), New York, The Bureau of Applied Social Research, Columbia University, 1958.

Lippman, H., Gerty, F., and Boyd, D. A., Jr.: Pastoral-psychiatric workshops: the St. John's Mental Health Institute, *The American Journal of Psychiatry, Vol. 115*: No. 6, 1958.

Noveck, Simon (ed.): *Judaism and Psychiatry,* New

York, The National Academy for Adult Jewish Studies of the United Synagogues of America, 1956.

10. This sentence makes reference in a few words to an enormous spread of information—concepts, theories and data. An introduction and orientation may be had through consulting the table of contents and also the subject index of:

Lindzey, Gardner (ed.): *Handbook of Social Psychology*, Cambridge, Mass., Addison-Wesley, 1954.

"Ethology" refers to the comparative study of behavior patterns in different species of animals with special emphasis on development. Most pertinent to the interest of the psychiatrist are findings with regard to how the experiences of a young bird or mammal may have persistent effects on behavior all the rest of the individual's life. It is possible, for instance, so to manipulate the environment at a critical period of development as to render an animal a more or less social isolate among his own kind. See:

Bowlby, John: Symposium on the contribution of current theories to an understanding of child development (I) an ethological approach to research in child development, *The British Journal of Medical Psychology*, Vol. 30, Part 4, 1957.

Lorenz, K. Z.: *King Solomon's Ring*, New York, Thomas Y. Crowell Co., 1952 (an account very entertainingly told for the general public).

Scott, John Paul: *Animal Behavior*, (especially chapters 6, 7 and 8) Chicago, The University of Chicago Press, 1958.

Tinbergen, N.: *Social Behavior in Animals*, London, Methuen, 1953.

11. There have been a number of previous definitions of social psychiatry, some representing a considerably different emphasis from that which has been formulated in this book. Thus, the words have been used to refer to combinations of social work and psychiatry, to the activities of sociologists in problems bearing on mental health and mental illness, to the work of other behavioral scientists in the same field and to essentially clinical efforts toward helping a patient adjust to the social environment in which he finds himself. A recent statement from the World Health Organization along this line says:

"social psychiatry refers to the preventive and curative measures which are directed towards fitting the individual for a satisfactory and useful life in terms of his own social environment. In order to achieve this goal, social psychiatry attempts to provide the mentally ill, and those in danger of becoming so, opportunities for establishing contacts with society which are favourable to the maintenance of social adequacy."

See:
Social psychiatry and community attitudes, *Technical Report Series, No. 177*, Geneva, World Health Organization, 1959. I would call this "Socializing Psychiatry" rather than "Social Psychiatry."

For other definitions see:
Baruk, Henri: *La Psychiatrie Sociale*, Paris, Presses Universitaires de France, 1955, pp. 5-9.

Bernard, Paul: Socio-psychiatrie, evénements sociaux et psychiatrie in *Encyclopédie Médico-chirurgicale*, 18, rue Séguier, Paris.

Diethelm, Oskar: Social psychiatry in North America, *Psychiatrie und Gesellschaft*, Ehrhardt, H., Ploog, D.,

Stutte, H. (eds.), Bern und Stuttgart, Hans Huber, 1958.

Dunham, Warren H.: The field of social psychiatry, in Rose, Arnold M. (ed.), *Mental Health and Mental Disorder*, New York, W. W. Norton, 1955.

Leighton, A. H., Clausen, J. A. and Wilson, R. N. (eds.): *Explorations in Social Psychiatry*, New York, Basic Books, 1957, p. 4, footnote.

Lewis, Nolan D. C.: American psychiatry from its beginnings to world war II, in *American Handbook of Psychiatry*, Arieti, S. (ed.), New York, Basic Books, 1959, p. 11.

Mora, George: Recent American psychiatric developments, in *American Handbook of Psychiatry*, Arieti, S. (ed.), New York, Basic Books, 1959, p. 44.

Opler, M. K.: *Culture, Psychiatry and Human Values*, Springfield, Charles C Thomas, 1956, p. 140 and 177.

Rennie, T. A. C.: Social psychiatry—a definition, in *The International Journal of Social Psychiatry, Vol. 1*: No. 1, p. 12, Summer 1955.

Rosen, George: Social stress and mental disease from the eighteenth century to the present: some origins of social, psychiatry, in *The Milbank Memorial Fund Quarterly Vol. XXXVII*, No. 1, p.5, 1959.

Schermerhorn, R. A.: Social Psychiatry, in Rose, Arnold M. (ed.), *Mental Health and Mental Disorder*, New York, W. W. Norton, 1955.

12. For an introductory outline to the work of Snow and Budd, see:

Rosen, George: *A History of Public Health*, New York, MD Publications, Inc., 1958, pp. 285-287.

13. Gruenberg has pointed out that, as in the public

health approach to illness, three kinds of psychiatric prevention may be distinguished. The first is "Primary Prevention," which consists in preventing "what we know how to prevent" and is evidently the same as that outlined here as "genuinely preventive." The next is "Secondary Prevention" which aims at early diagnosis and effective treatment. The last is "Tertiary Prevention" and is concerned with the reduction of disability. Gruenberg feels that none of these are being carried out to the extent they could and should be. See:

> Gruenberg, Ernest M.: Application of control methods to mental illness, *American Journal of Public Health*, *Vol. 47*: No. 8, August, 1957.

14. Relatively little of the work done in this field has been reported in publications. We may note, however, that firms such as E. D. Chapple & Co., of New York and Social Research Inc., of Chicago have been set up to do consulting in human relations problems in industry. Corporations that have had their own personnel specializing in research into these problems include Sears, Roebuck & Co., General Electric, Bell Telephone, and Standard Oil of New Jersey.

15. For reference to culture-technological change programs in which there has been participation by a psychiatrist, see:

> Bunker, Robert and Adair, John: *The First Look at Strangers*, New Brunswick, N. J., Rutgers University Press, 1959.
>
> Fried, Jacob: Acculturation and mental health among Indian migrants in Peru, in Marvin K. Opler, (ed.) *Culture and Mental Health*, New York, The Macmillan Company, 1959, pp. 119-137.

Leighton, Alexander H., and Leighton, Dorothea C.: *The Navaho Door* (*An Introduction to Navaho Life*), Cambridge, Mass., Harvard University Press, 1944.

Lin, Tsung-Yi: Two types of delinquent youth in Chinese society, in Opler, Marvin K., (ed.), *Culture and Mental Health,* New York, The Macmillan Company, 1959, pp. 257-271.

Spicer, Edward H. (ed.): *Human Problems in Technological Change,* New York, Russell Sage Foundation, 1952.

A meeting of thirty specialists of varying backgrounds to discuss mental health problems of the population sou*h of the Sahara is reported in:

International Research Newsletter in Ment a Health, *Vol. I*: No. 1, p. 3, 1959, published by tne Postgraduate Center for Psychotherapy, New York.

Also of interest in this field is a *Review and Newsletter* concerning transcultural research in mental health problems, published by the Department of Psychiatry, McGill University, 1025 Pine Avenue West, Montreal, Canada.

16. A discussion of Hume and Kant in regard to these points may be found in:

Aiken, Henry D. (ed.): Chapter II, The transcendental turn in modern philosophy, *The Age of Ideology,* New York, Mentor Books, 1956.

See also:

Hume, David: Section VII of the idea of necessary connection, *An Inquiry Concerning Human Understanding,* Hendel, Charles W. (ed.), New York, Liberal Arts Press, 1955.

Smith, Norman Kemp (translator): *Immanuel Kant's Critique of Pure Reason,* London, Macmillan and Co., 1950. Of particular relevance is Chapter III on The ground of the distinction of all objects in general into phenomena and noumena.

17. For Kurt Lewin's essay on Aristotelian and Galilean modes of thought, see:
Lewin, Kurt: *Dynamic Theory of Personality,* Chapter I. New York, McGraw-Hill, 1935.

18. See:
Dantzig, Tobias, *The Bequest of the Greeks,* Chapter III on the genesis of geometry, London, George Allen and Urwin, 1955.

19. For some amusing remarks along the lines of this discussion, see:
Stefanson, Vilhjarmur: *The Standardization of Error,* (Psyche Miniature Series), London, Kegan Paul, Trench, Trubner and Co., 1928.
With regard to chromosomes see Tijo, J. H., and Levan, A.: The chromosome number in man, *Hereditas Vol. 42,* No. 1, 1956.

20. For reviews and critical comment pertinent to these trends see:
Becker, Howard and Barnes, Harry Elmer: *Social Thought from Lore to Science,* Washington, D.C., Harren Press, 1952.
Karpf, Fay B.: *American Social Psychology,* New York, McGraw-Hill, 1932.
Also:
Hawley, Amos H.: *Human Ecology, A Theory of Community Structure,* New York, Ronald Press, 1950, pp. 50-51.

The influence of Helmholtz on Freud is shown in Jones, Ernest, *The Life and Work of Sigmund Freud, Volume I,* New York, Basic Books, pp. 41, 245, 258, 369 and 385.

21. See:

MacMahon, Brian: Physical Damage to the foetus, in *Causes of Mental Disorders: A Review of Epidemiology Knowledge 1959,* New York, Milbank Memorial Fund (in preparation) 1960.

22. For a general review of the modern scene and for a bibliography, see:

Gruenberg, Ernest M. and Bellin, Seymour S.: The impact of mental disease on society, in *Explorations in Social Psychiatry,* Alexander H. Leighton, John A. Clausen, and Robert N. Wilson (eds.), New York, Basic Books, 1957, pp. 341-364.

Guttmacher and Weihofen describe George III as suffering from manic-depressive disorder and say that his third attack in 1801 was "clearly precipitated by political crisis. George III sorrowfully accepted Pitt's resignation rather than accede to Irish Union, which would have meant permitting Catholics to serve in Parliament and to hold important state offices. In a week he was in a full-blown manic excitement. After his recovery his ministers dropped the issue rather than chance producing another psychosis. As a result, social progress was seriously obstructed for a generation." (Guttmacher, Manfred and Weihofen, Henry: *Psychiatry and the Law,* New York, Norton, 1952, p. 71.)

With regard to Nietzsche, Crane Brinton has observed that he had "an excellent mind, well if rather bookishly trained, great aesthetic sensibility, a natural gift for writing, strong emotions which he could focus in the *saeva indignatio* we often call moral purpose, an untrained body, an unstable nervous system, a total personality never successfully conditioned to *living together* with anyone—not in the family, not in the occupational or social group, not in church or state. He had, finally, a devouring ambition to be admired, a thirst for disciples, a will to shine which, as the Will to Power, he built up into a characteristic philosophical ultimate, and which, syphilis aiding, ended in paranoia." (Brinton, Crane: *Nietzsche,* Cambridge, Mass., Harvard University Press, 1941, pp. 167-168.) ". . . he was too bitten with reforming zeal, too impatient, too exalted, perhaps at bottom too insanely or divinely convinced that he alone was the measure of all things, to accept the humbling limitations imposed by regard for facts. And so he made his unhappy down-going and over-going to that strangest of 'true worlds,' the world of the supermen . . . . Nietzsche called for the Supermen. Mussolini and Hitler answered the call. It does not much matter that in all probability Nietzsche would have scorned them as perverters of his doctrine, would have opposed them bitterly." (*Ibid.*, p. 171.)

René Fueloep-Miller, among others, has commented upon the possible relationship between Dostoevsky's epileptic seizures and his creativity and effectiveness as a writer. Thus it is said that "the unrest preceding attacks, to which he owed his most intense psychic experiences and visions, decisively influenced his whole creative life." (Fueloep-Miller, René: *Fyodor Dostoevsky,* New York, Charles Scribner's Sons, 1950, p. 35.)

Similarly Ivanov, after giving a long list of the "revelations" Dostoevsky seeks to express in his writings, remarks that these were under the influence of "premonitions" which were "unmistakable precursors of Dostoevsky's attacks of epilepsy—that disease . . . which seems to possess the power of obliterating the boundaries between idealism and realism; so that at moments the outer world becomes the inner, whilst conversely the inner world becomes alien and remote, and seems like a miraculous drama in the distance." (Ivanov, Vyacheslav: *Freedom and the Tragic Life, A Study in Dostoevsky,* New York, Noonday Press, 1952, p. 37.)

23. See:

Kubie, Lawrence S.: Social forces and the neurotic process, in *Explorations in Social Psychiatry,* Alexander H. Leighton, John A. Clausen, and Robert N. Wilson (eds.), New York, Basic Books, 1957, pp. 77-104.

24. For a more extended discussion of etiology in psychiatric disorder in relation to sociocultural environment, see:

Leighton, A. H.: *My Name is Legion* (Vol. I of the Stirling County Study of Psychiatric Disorder and Sociocultural Environment), New York, Basic Books, 1959.

25. This is Volume III of the Stirling County Study. For an account of the purpose and concepts of this study, see:

Leighton, A. H.: *My Name is Legion* (Vol. I of the Stirling County Study of Psychiatric Disorder and Sociocultural Environment), New York, Basic Books, 1959, especially Chapters IV to VII.

26. A more complete account of this hypothesis may be found in:

Leighton, A. H.: *My Name is Legion* (Vol. I of the Stirling County Study of Psychiatric Disorder and Sociocultural Environment), New York, Basic Books, 1959, Chapters VIII and IX.

27. See:

Langner, Thomas S.: Environmental stress and mental health, in *Epidemiology of Mental Disorders,* Hoch, Paul H. and Zubin, Joseph (eds.), New York, Grune & Stratton, 1960 (in press).

Three volumes reporting this study in full are now in preparation and it is expected that the first will appear early in 1961. The tentative title is *Midtown Manhattan - The Mental Health Story.* The authors of the series are T.A.C. Rennie, Leo Srole, Thomas S. Langner and Marvin K. Opler. The publisher is Mc-Graw-Hill.

28. See, for example:

Coleman, Jules V.: Mental health consultation to agencies protecting family life, in *The Elements of a Community Mental Health Program,* New York, Milbank Memorial Fund, 1956, pp. 69-76.

Davis, Kingsley: Mental hygiene and the class structure, in *Mental Health and Mental Disorder,* Rose, Arnold M. (ed.), New York, W. W. Norton, 1955 pp. 578-598.

Hollingshead, August B., and Redlich, Frederick C., *Social Class and Mental Illness,* New York, John Wiley & Sons, 1958, especially p. 275.

THE THOMAS WILLIAM SALMON
MEMORIAL LECTURES

The Salmon Lectures of the New York Academy of Medicine were established in 1931, as a memorial to Thomas William Salmon, M.D., and for the advancement of the objects to which his professional career had been wholly devoted.

Dr. Salmon died in 1927, at the age of 51, after a career of extraordinary service in psychiatric practice and education, and in the development of a world-wide movement for the better treatment and prevention of mental disorders, and for the promotion of mental health.

Following his death, a group of his many friends organized a committee for the purpose of establishing one or more memorials that might serve to preserve and pass on to future generations some of the spirit and purpose of his supremely noble and useful life. Five hundred and ninety-six subscriptions were received, three hundred and nineteen from physicians.

Of the amount thus obtained, $100,000 was, on January 10, 1931, given to the New York Academy of Medicine, as a fund to provide an income for the support of an annual series of lectures and for other projects for the advancement of psychiatry and mental hygiene. For the purpose of giving lasting quality to the lectures as a memorial to Dr. Salmon, and of extending their usefulness, it was stipulated that each series should be published in a bound volume of which this volume is one.

Lectures Published in this Series

Psychobiology *By Adolf Meyer*,
Published posthumously.
Destiny and Disease in Mental Disorders *By C. Macfie Campbell*
Twentieth Century Psychiatry *By William A. White*

Reading, Writing and Speech Problems in Children
By Samuel Torrey Orton
Personality in Formation and Action *By William Healy*
Psychopathic States *By David K. Henderson*
Beyond the Clinical Frontiers *By Edward A. Strecker*
A Short History of Psychiatric Achievement *By Nolan D. C. Lewis*
Psychological Effects of War on Citizen and Soldier
By Robert D. Gillespie
Psychiatry in War *By Emilio Mira*
Freud's Contribution to Psychiatry *By Abraham Arden Brill*
The Shaping of Psychiatry by War *By John Rawlings Rees*
The Biology of Schizophrenia *By Roy Graham Hoskins*
New Fields of Psychiatry *By David Mordecai Levy*
Power and Personality *By Harold Dwight Lasswell*
Cell Growth and Cell Function *By Torbjoern O. Caspersson*
Emotions and Clinical Medicine *By Stanley Cobb*
Frontal Lobotomy and Affective Behavior *By John Farquhar Fulton*
Heredity in Health and Mental Disorder *By Franz Josef Kallmann*
Culture and Mental Disorders *By Ralph Linton*
Psychiatry Education and Progress *By John C. Whitehorn*